HORNGREN'S ACCOUNTING

Tenth Canadian Edition
Volume 1

Tracie L. Miller-Nobles

Brenda Mattison

Ella Mae Matsumura

Carol A. Meissner

Jo-Ann L. Johnston

Peter R. Norwood

flexText

PEARSON

Toronto

Editorial Director: Claudine O'Donnell
Acquisitions Editor: Megan Farrell
Marketing Manager: Claire Varley
Program Manager: Karen Townsend
Project Manager: Pippa Kennard
Developmental Editor: Steven Lee
Composition: Cenveo® Publishing Services

Vice-President, Cross Media and Publishing Services: Gary Bennett

7   17

ISBN: 978-0-13-457654-1

Contents

Preface

Faculty

Welcome to Pearson's *flexText* for Horngren's Accounting 10th Canadian Edition. This student solution not only supports in-class work, but is also one of the many tools that Pearson has published to support various teaching strategies.

The *flexText* facilitates the flipped classroom approach to course delivery, where you might spend a portion of class time having students work either individually or in groups on guided problems. If a fully flipped class isn't your goal, but you still want to give students time in class to work on guided problem-solving exercises, this tool can be used to achieve that as well.

Students

Here is another tool to add to your toolkit for success. Read the full e-text and practice some questions online. Then in the classroom, get a near-to-real-world experience of using pencil and paper to prepare for tests.

Remember, the key to success in learning any new task is practice, practice, practice. The *flexText* will help you do this more efficiently because the questions are shown right where you work on the answers. It also keeps your work all neat and organized because the working papers are already formatted and ordered for you.

Pearson *flexText*: A Key for Success in School and at Work

Regardless of the course you're taking—whether you are in General Business, Marketing, Entrepreneurship, Accounting, Human Resources, or any other program—you will want to leave with skills that can help you get the job you want. Some of these skills will be specific to your course of study or major. These are basic skills your employers will want you to have. An accountant, for example, will be expected to know how to read a balance sheet and write journal entries. However, there are other skills essential to your success in the workplace that might not seem so obvious but are important enough that some governments call them "Essential" Employability Skills. The Conference Board of Canada goes even further, calling them "the skills you need to enter, stay in, and progress in the world of work—whether you work on your own or as a part of a team." (http://www.conferenceboard.ca/topics/education/learning-tools/employability-skills.aspx)

This Pearson *flexText* was designed to help you develop these skills.

What are Essential Employability Skills?

Essential Employability Skills can be grouped into six broad categories: Communication, Numeracy, Critical Thinking & Problem Solving, Information Management, Interpersonal, and Personal. The government of Ontario thinks that these skills are so important that they expect everyone who graduates with a certificate or diploma to have them. Other provincial governments place an equal emphasis on them as well. Many of these skills are also referred to as "soft skills," or "21st century skills," and represent areas like writing that are not specific to the core content of any one course but are important to your success in *all* courses, and in the working world. Being able to show prospective employers that you have these skills can make a huge difference in your ability to get the job that you want.

Pearson's *flexText* is designed with the needs of college students in mind, including the need to develop and demonstrate Essential Employability Skills. Here's how.

COMMUNICATION SKILLS

Defining skill areas: reading, writing, speaking, listening, presenting, and visual literacy

One of the reasons why students don't develop their reading skills is simply because they have not bought their textbooks at all. *flexTexts* are affordable, and available at a price that will encourage as many students as possible to buy—and read—their course materials. *flexTexts* often include short answer questions or writing activities that provide opportunities for students to practice and develop their written communication skills.

NUMERACY SKILLS

Defining skill areas: understanding and applying mathematical concepts and reasoning, analyzing and using mathematical data, and conceptualizing

flexTexts in disciplines such as Accounting require students to understand and apply some mathematical concepts when answering practice questions. The spiral bound *flexText* format encourages their use as in-class activity workbooks, where faculty can provide instructional support to students as they work through these problems.

CRITICAL THINKING & PROBLEM SOLVING SKILLS

Defining skill areas: analyzing, synthesizing, evaluating, decision making, and creative and innovative thinking

The exercises and activities found in Pearson's *flexTexts* are not simply factual, recall, or "skill and drill" type activities. They are created to engage students at many different levels of Bloom's Taxonomy to help develop their critical thinking and problem solving skills. And because the *flexText* is affordable, a greater number of students can purchase their course materials, gaining the opportunity to develop these skills through practice.

INFORMATION MANAGEMENT SKILLS

Defining skill areas: gathering and managing information, selecting and using appropriate tools and technology for a task or project, computer literacy, and internet skills

Not all of the exercises in a *flexText* are pencil and paper activities. Some also require students to engage with applications such as Microsoft Excel, or to explain how they would utilize these tools to find the solution to a problem.

INTERPERSONAL SKILLS

Defining skill areas: teamwork, relationship management, conflict resolution, leadership, and networking

Because *flexTexts* are designed to be used in class, they facilitate group work and collaborative problem solving. Activities that, in the past, would have been assigned as homework to be done individually can now be implemented in ways that help students develop their interpersonal skills.

PERSONAL SKILLS

Defining skill areas: managing self, managing change and being flexible and adaptable, engaging in reflexive practice, and demonstrating personal responsibility

Making the decision to purchase course materials and actively engage with course content is one of the first steps towards demonstrating a degree of personal responsibility for success in school. The page layout of a *flexText* also encourages note-taking and supports the development of good study skills.

1 ACCOUNTING AND THE BUSINESS ENVIRONMENT

LEARNING OBJECTIVES

1 Define accounting, and describe the users of accounting information.
2 Compare and contrast the forms of business organizations.
3 Describe some concepts and principles of accounting.
4 Use the accounting equation to analyze business transactions.
5 Prepare financial statements.
6 Briefly explain the different accounting standards.

Learning Objectives are a "roadmap" showing what will be covered and what is especially important in each chapter.

Starter 1–3 ①

Learning Objectives appear beside each Starter, Exercise, and Problem.

For each of the users of accounting information, indicate whether they are an external decision maker (E) or an internal decision maker. (I).

a. Marketing manager _____

b. Canada Revenue Agency _____

c. Investor _____

d. Controller _____

e. Supplier _____

Starter 1–5 ③

Match the assumption, principle, or constraint description with the appropriate term by placing a, b, c, d, e, and f on the appropriate line.

a. Cost principle of measurement   _____   Benefits of the information produced by an accounting system must be greater than the costs

b. Going concern assumption   _____   Amounts may be ignored if the effect on a decision maker's decision is not significant

c. Stable monetary unit assumption   _____   Transactions are recorded based on the cash amount received or paid

d. Economic entity assumption   _____   Ignore the effects of inflation in the accounting records

e. Cost–benefit constraint   _____   Assumes that a business is going to continue operations indefinitely

f. Materiality constraint   _____   A business must keep its accounting records separate from its owner's accounting records

Most **Questions** with the number formatted like this are available for additional practice in MyAccountingLab.

Starter 1–11 ⑤

Determine the expenses for September based on the following data:

September net income $10,000
Beginning owner's equity $25,000
Owner's withdrawals .... $ 5,000
Ending owner's equity $30,000
September revenue $42,000

_____

_____

_____

_____

_____

Exercise 1–2 ②

Indicate whether each statement below applies to a sole proprietorship, a partnership, or a corporation.

a. The life of the business is limited by the death of the owner.

b. Each owner is personally liable for claims against the business.

c. A business in which there is only one owner and "he or she is the business."

d. Owners are not personally liable for claims against the business.

e. The form of business typically used by accountants and lawyers.

f. Ownership is easily transferred in a public exchange.

g. Canadian Tire and Tim Hortons are examples of this form of business.

_____

_____

_____

_____

_____

_____

_____

_____

_____

_____

_____

_____

_____

_____

_____

_____

_____

Exercise 1–4 ④

Complete the following chart for the selected transactions for Martha's Muffins shown below.

a. Martha invests $10,000 cash into a business known as Martha's Muffins.

b. Martha purchases baking supplies on account for $500.

c. Martha receives and pays the kitchen's utilities bill amounting to $425.

d. Sales revenue for the current period amounts to $2,000 (all revenue transactions involved cash).

e. Martha purchases a new fridge for $3,500 cash.

	Assets	Liabilities	Owner's Equity
a)			
b)			
c)			
d)			
e)			
Totals			

Exercise 1–6   ④

Compute the missing amount in the accounting equation for each business.

> Make lots of notes in the margins so you can study from them later. Here you need to remember that A = L + OE.

	Assets	=	Liabilities	+	Owner's Equity
Economy Cuts	_____		$120,000		$40,000
Marpole Dry Cleaners	$100,000		_____		$50,000
Dauphin Gift and Cards	$145,000		$115,000		_____

_____

_____

_____

_____

_____

_____

_____

_____

_____

_____

_____

_____

_____

_____

_____

_____

Exercise 1–8   ④

Indicate the effects of the following business transactions on the accounting equation of a proprietorship. Transaction *a* is answered as a guide.

a. Received $50,000 cash from the owner.

    Answer: Increase asset (Cash)

        Increase owner's equity (Owner, Capital)

b. Paid the current month's office rent of $4,000.

c. Paid $3,500 cash to purchase office supplies.

d. Performed engineering services for a client on account, $6,000.

e. Purchased office furniture on account at a cost of $5,000.

f. Received cash on account, $3,000.

g. Paid cash on account, $2,500.

h. Sold land for $50,000 cash, which was the business's cost of the land.

i. Performed engineering services for a client and received cash of $6,000.

a. – i.

a. Increase asset (Cash)

Increase owner's equity (Owner, Capital)

Exercise 1–9 ④

Gayle Hayashi, M.D., opens a medical clinic. During her first month of operation, January, the clinic, entitled Hayashi Medical Clinic, experienced the following events:

Jan.		
	6	Hayashi invested $250,000 in the clinic by opening a bank account in the name of Hayashi Medical Clinic.
	9	Hayashi Medical Clinic paid cash for land costing $150,000. There are plans to build a clinic on the land. Until then, the business will rent an office.
	12	The clinic purchased medical supplies for $10,000 on account.
	15	On January 15, Hayashi Medical Clinic officially opened for business.
	15–31	During the rest of the month, the clinic earned professional fees of $20,000 and received cash immediately.
	15–31	The clinic paid cash expenses: employee salaries, $5,000; office rent, $4,000; utilities, $500.
	28	The clinic sold supplies to another clinic at cost for $1,000.
	31	The clinic paid $4,000 on the account from January 12.

Required   Analyze the effects of these events on the accounting equation of Hayashi Medical Clinic.

Analysis of Transactions

DATE	ASSETS			=	LIABILITIES	+	OWNER'S EQUITY	
	CASH	+	MEDICAL SUPPLIES	+	LAND	=	ACCOUNTS PAYABLE	+	G. HAYASHI, CAPITAL	TYPE OF OWNER'S EQUITY TRANSACTION

Some charts have information filled in **to save you time** so you can focus on the important parts of the questions.

Exercise 1–11 ④ ⑤

The accounting records of Chiang Consulting Services contain the following accounts:

Supplies Expense	Accounts Payable
Accounts Receivable	Rent Expense
J. Chiang, Capital	Cash
Salary Expense	J. Chiang, Withdrawals
Computer Equipment	Supplies
Consulting Service Revenue	Notes Payable

Required

1. Indicate whether each account listed is a(n) asset (A), liability (L), owner's equity (OE), revenue (R), or expense (E) account.
2. Indicate whether each account listed appears on the balance sheet (B), income statement (I), statement of owner's equity (SOE), or cash flow statement (CF). Some accounts can appear on more than one statement.

	1. Type of Account	2. Statement
Supplies Expense		
Accounts Receivable		
J. Chiang, Capital		
Salary Expense		
Computer Equipment		
Consulting Service Revenue		
Accounts Payable		
Rent Expense		
Cash		
J. Chiang, Withdrawals		
Supplies		
Notes Payable		

Exercise 1–15 ⑤

Examine Exhibit 1–11. The exhibit summarizes the transactions of Hunter Environmental Consulting for the month of April 2016. Suppose the business completed Transactions 1 to 7 and needed a bank loan on April 21, 2016. The vice-president of the bank requires financial statements to support all loan requests.

Required Prepare the income statement, statement of owner's equity, and balance sheet that Hunter Environmental Consulting would present to the banker on April 21, 2016, after completing the first seven transactions.

> When the question requires additional information, it is provided so you do not have to refer back to the textbook.

EXHIBIT 1–11 | Analysis of Transactions of Hunter Environmental Consulting

PANEL A: DETAILS OF TRANSACTIONS

(1) The business recorded the $250,000 cash investment made by Lisa Hunter.
(2) Paid $100,000 cash for land.
(3) Bought $7,000 of office supplies on account.
(4) Received $30,000 cash from clients for service revenue earned.
(5) Performed services for clients on account, $25,000.
(6) Paid cash expenses: rent, $4,000; employee salaries, $6,500; utilities, $1,500.
(7) Paid $5,000 on the account payable created in Transaction 3.
(8) Remodelled Hunter's personal residence. This is not a transaction of the business.
(9) Collected $15,000 on the account receivable created in Transaction 5.
(10) The business paid $6,000 cash to Hunter as a withdrawal.

PANEL B: ANALYSIS OF TRANSACTIONS

	Cash	+ Accounts Receivable	+ Office Supplies	+ Land		Accounts Payable +	Lisa Hunter, Capital	Type of Owner's Equity Transaction
(1)	+250,000						+250,000	Owner investment
Bal.	250,000						250,000	
(2)	−100,000			+100,000				
Bal.	150,000			100,000			250,000	
(3)			+7,000			+7,000		
Bal.	150,000		7,000	100,000		7,000	250,000	
(4)	+30,000						+30,000	Service revenue
Bal.	180,000		7,000	100,000		7,000	280,000	
(5)		+25,000					+25,000	Service revenue
Bal.	180,000	25,000	7,000	100,000	=	7,000	305,000	
(6)	−4,000						−4,000	Rent expense
	−6,500						−6,500	Salaries expense
	−1,500						−1,500	Utilities expense
Bal.	168,000	25,000	7,000	100,000		7,000	293,000	
(7)	−5,000					−5,000		
Bal.	163,000	25,000	7,000	100,000		2,000	293,000	
(8)	Not a transaction of the business							
(9)	+15,000	−15,000						
Bal.	178,000	10,000	7,000	100,000		2,000	293,000	
(10)	−6,000						−6,000	Owner withdrawal
Bal.	172,000	10,000	7,000	100,000		2,000	287,000	

Assets = 289,000   Liabilities + Owner's Equity = 289,000

Exercise 1-17

Michael Lee started his new executive coaching business on June 1. Lee Management
Consulting completed the following transactions during June 2016:

> Look for Lee Management Consulting in each chapter. This Serial Exercise question follows the same company throughout your course.

Jun.	2	Received $25,000 cash from owner Michael Lee. The business gave owner's equity in the business to Lee.
	2	Lee found a great downtown loft from which to operate. He paid cash for rent for the month of June, $3,000.
	3	Paid cash for a laptop, $1,000. The computer is expected to remain in service for four years. (Use the Equipment account for this transaction.)
	4	Purchased office furniture on account, $5,000. The furniture is expected to last for five years.
	5	Purchased supplies on account, $500.
	9	Performed consulting services for a client on account, $3,000.
	12	Paid utility expenses with cash, $250
	18	Performed consulting services for a client and received cash of $2,000.
	21	Received $2,000 in advance for client services to be performed at a rate of $100 per day for a period of 20 days. (Use the liability account Unearned Revenue for this transaction. We will learn more about this account in Chapter 3.)
	22	Hired an office manager on a part-time basis. She will be paid $2,000 per month. She started work on Monday, June 25.
	23	Paid $500 cash for the supplies purchased on June 5.
	26	Collected a partial payment of $1,500 from the consulting client invoiced on June 9.
	28	Michael Lee withdrew $2,000 cash for personal use.

Required Analyze the effects of Lee Management Consulting's transactions on the accounting equation.

Analysis of Transactions

DATE	ASSETS					=	LIABILITIES		+	OWNER'S EQUITY	
	CASH	ACCOUNTS RECEIVABLE	SUPPLIES	EQUIPMENT	FURNITURE		ACCOUNTS PAYABLE	UNEARNED REVENUE		MICHAEL LEE, CAPITAL	TYPE OF OWNER'S EQUITY TRANSACTION

TOTAL ASSETS = $ _____   TOTAL LIABILITIES AND OWNER'S EQUITY = $ _____

14   Chapter 1

Exercise 1–18 ④ ⑤

Compute the missing amounts for each of the following businesses:

	Fraser Co.	Delta Co.	Pine Co.
Beginning:			
Assets..	$350,000	$300,000	$540,000
Liabilities..	200,000	120,000	360,000
Ending:			
Assets..	$500,000	$360,000	$?
Liabilities..	250,000	160,000	480,000
Owner's equity:			
Investments by owner............................	$?	$ 0	$ 50,000
Withdrawals by owner............................	250,000	150,000	220,000
Income Statement:			
Revenues...	$660,000	$350,000	$900,000
Expenses...	460,000	?	675,000

Calculations:

ACCOUNT	FRASER CO.	DELTA CO.	PINE CO.

Problem 1–2A ③ ④

Jon Conlin was a lawyer and partner in a large firm, a partnership, for five years after graduating from university. Recently, he resigned his position to open his own legal practice, which he operates as a proprietorship. The name of the new company is Conlin & Associates.

Conlin recorded the following events during the organizing phase of his new business and its first month of operations. Some of the events were personal and did not affect the legal practice. Others were business transactions and should be accounted for by the business.

Jul.	4	Conlin received $100,000 cash from his former partners in the firm from which he resigned.
	5	Conlin invested $50,000 cash in his business, Conlin & Associates.
	5	The business paid office rent expense for the month of July, $3,000.
	6	The business paid $1,000 cash for letterhead stationery for the office.
	7	The business purchased office furniture on account for $7,000, promising to pay within six months.
	10	Conlin sold 2,000 shares of Royal Bank stock, which he had owned for several years, receiving $25,000 cash from his stockbroker.
	11	Conlin deposited the $25,000 cash from the sale of the Royal Bank shares in his personal bank account.
	12	A representative of a large construction company telephoned Conlin and told him of the company's intention to transfer its legal business to Conlin & Associates.
	29	The business provided legal services for a client and submitted the bill for services, $10,000. The business expected to collect from this client within two weeks.
	31	Conlin withdrew $3,000 cash from the business.

Required

1. Classify each of the preceding events as one of the following (list each date, then choose a, b, or c):

   a. A business transaction to be accounted for by the business, Conlin & Associates.

   b. A business-related event but not a transaction to be accounted for by Conlin & Associates.

   c. A personal transaction not to be accounted for by Conlin & Associates.

2. Analyze the effects of the above events on the accounting equation of Conlin & Associates.

Requirement 1

CLASSIFICATION OF TRANSACTIONS

July 4 _____   July 10 _____

5 _____   11 _____

5 _____   12 _____

6 _____   29 _____

7 _____   31 _____

Requirement 2

Analysis of Transactions

DATE	ASSETS				= LIABILITIES +	OWNER'S EQUITY	
	CASH	+ ACCOUNTS RECEIVABLE	+ SUPPLIES	+ OFFICE FURNITURE	= ACCOUNTS PAYABLE	+ J. CONLIN, CAPITAL	TYPE OF OWNER'S EQUITY TRANSACTION

Problem 1–5A ⑤

Presented below are the amounts of (a) the assets and liabilities of Canadian Gardening Consultants as of December 31, 2017, and (b) the revenues and expenses of the company for the year ended December 31, 2017. The items are listed in alphabetical order.

Accounts Payable	$ 57,000	Insurance Expense	$ 4,500
Accounts Receivable	36,000	Interest Expense	15,000
Advertising Expense	48,500	Land	37,500
Building	300,000	Note Payable	195,000
Cash	15,000	Salary Expense	240,000
Computer Equipment	165,000	Salary Payable	22,500
Courier Expense	7,000	Service Revenue	450,000
Furniture	45,000	Supplies	7,500

The opening balance of owner's equity was $300,000. At year end, after the calculation of net income, the owner, Jin Wu, withdrew $103,500.

Required

1. Prepare the business's income statement for the year ended December 31, 2017.
2. Prepare the statement of owner's equity of the business for the year ended December 31, 2017.
3. Prepare the balance sheet of the business at December 31, 2017.
4. Answer these questions about the business:
   a. Was the result of operations for the year a profit or a loss? How much was it?
   b. Did the business's owner's equity increase or decrease during the year? How would this affect the business's ability to borrow money from a bank in the future?
   c. How much in total economic resources does the business have at December 31, 2017, as it moves into the new year? How much does the business owe? What is the dollar amount of the owner's portion of the business at December 31, 2017?

Requirement 1

Requirement 2

Requirement 3

Requirements 4 a. – c.

Problem 1–7A ④ ⑤

Mary Reaney is the proprietor of a career counselling and employee search business, Reaney Personnel Services. The following amounts summarize the financial position of the business on August 31, 2017:

	Cash	+	Accounts Receivable	+	Supplies	+	Furniture and Computers	=	Accounts Payable	+	M. Reaney, Capital
				Assets				=	Liabilities	+	Owner's Equity
Bal.	40,000		35,000				95,000		55,000		115,000

During September 2017 the following company transactions occurred:

a. Reaney deposited $80,000 cash in the business bank account.

b. Performed services for a client and received cash of $5,000.

c. Paid off the August 31 balance of accounts payable.

d. Purchased supplies on account, $6,000.

e. Collected cash from a customer on account, $7,500.

f. Consulted on a large downsizing by a major corporation and billed the client for services rendered, $48,000.

g. Recorded the following business expenses for the month:
   (1) Paid office rent for September 2017—$5,000.
   (2) Paid advertising—$3,000.

h. Sold supplies to another business for $1,000 cash, which was the cost of the supplies.

i. Reaney withdrew $8,000 cash.

Required

1. Analyze the effects of the above transactions on the accounting equation of Reaney Personnel Services.

2. Prepare the income statement of Reaney Personnel Services for the month ended September 30, 2017. List expenses in decreasing order of amount.

3. Prepare the business's statement of owner's equity for the month ended September 30, 2017.

4. Prepare the balance sheet of Reaney Personnel Services at September 30, 2017.

Requirement 1

Analysis of Transactions

DATE	ASSETS					=	LIABILITIES	+	OWNER'S EQUITY	
	CASH	+	ACCOUNTS RECEIVABLE	+	SUPPLIES	+	FURNITURE & COMPUTERS	=	ACCOUNTS PAYABLE	+	M. REANEY, CAPITAL		TYPE OF OWNER'S EQUITY TRANSACTION

Requirement 2

Requirement 3

Requirement 4

Problem 1–8A ④ ⑤

Terrace Board Rentals was started on January 1, 2016, by Ryan Terrace with an investment of $50,000 cash. The company rents out snowboards and related gear from a small store. During the first 11 months, Terrace made additional investments of $20,000 and borrowed $40,000 from the bank. He did not withdraw any funds. The balance sheet accounts, excluding Terrace's capital account, at November 30, 2016, are as follows:

Cash...	$45,000
Accounts Receivable...	15,000
Rental Gear...	32,000
Rental Snowboards...	48,000
Store Equipment...	30,000
Accounts Payable..	12,000
Note Payable...	40,000

The following transactions took place during the month of December 2016:

Dec.	1	The business paid $5,000 for the month's rent on the store space.
	4	The business signed a one-year lease for the rental of additional store space at a cost of $4,000 per month. The lease is effective January 1. The business will pay the first month's rent in January.
	6	Rental revenues for the week were Gear, $4,000; Boards, $10,000. Three-quarters of the fees were paid in cash and the rest on account.
	10	The business paid the accounts payable from November 30, 2016.
	12	The business purchased gear for $20,000 and boards for $40,000, all on account.
	13	Rental revenues for the week were Gear, $7,000; Boards, $14,000. All the fees were paid in cash.
	15	The company received payment for the accounts receivable owing at November 30, 2016.
	18	The company purchased store equipment for $10,000 by paying $3,000 cash with the balance due in 60 days.

20	Rental revenues for the week were Gear, $8,000; Boards, $14,000. Half the fees were paid in cash and half on account.
21	Terrace withdrew $7,000.
24	The company paid the balance owing for the purchases made on December 12.
27	Rental revenues for the week were Gear, $6,000; Boards, $10,000. All the fees were paid in cash.
27	The company received payment for rental fees on account from December 6.
31	The company paid its employees for the month of December. The total wages expense was $10,000.
31	Terrace paid the utility bill for the month of December, which was $4,000.

Required

1. What is the total net income earned by the business over the period of January 1, 2016, to November 30, 2016?

2. Analyze the effects of the December 2016 transactions on the accounting equation of Terrace Board Rentals. Include the account balances from November 30, 2016.

3. Prepare the income statement for Terrace Board Rentals for the month ended December 31, 2016.

4. Prepare the statement of owner's equity for Terrace Board Rentals for the month ended December 31, 2016.

5. Prepare the balance sheet for Terrace Board Rentals at December 31, 2016.

6. Terrace has expressed concern that although the business seems to be profitable and growing, he constantly seems to be investing additional money into it. Prepare a reply to his concerns.

Requirement 1

Requirement 2

DATE	ASSETS					=	LIABILITIES		+	OWNER'S EQUITY	
	CASH	ACCOUNTS RECEIVABLE	RENTAL GEAR	RENTAL SNOWBOARDS	STORE EQUIPMENT		ACCOUNTS PAYABLE	NOTE PAYABLE		R. TERRACE, CAPITAL	TYPE OF OWNER'S EQUITY TRANSACTION
BAL	45,000	15,000	32,000	48,000	30,000		12,000	40,000		118,000	

Requirement 3

Requirement 4

Requirement 5

Requirement 6

2 RECORDING BUSINESS TRANSACTIONS

LEARNING OBJECTIVES

1 Define and use key accounting terms.
2 Apply the rules of debit and credit.
3 Analyze and record transactions in the journal.
4 Post from the journal to the ledger.
5 Prepare and use a trial balance.

Starter 2–1 ①

Put the steps in the accounting cycle in the proper sequence by inserting the numbers 1 to 11.

a. Prepare a post-closing trial balance   _____

b. Prepare an adjusted trial balance   _____

c. Identify and analyze the transaction   _____

d. Prepare the unadjusted trial balance   _____

e. Post adjusting journal entries to the ledger _____

f. Post from the journal to the ledger accounts _____

g. Journalize adjusting journal entries   _____

h. Journalize closing entries   _____

i. Prepare financial statements   _____

j. Post closing entries to the ledger   _____

k. Record transaction in a journal   _____

Starter 2–3 ①

Accounting has its own vocabulary and basic relationships. Match the accounting terms at left with the corresponding definitions at right.

_____	1. Credit	A. Record of transactions
_____	2. Normal balance	B. Always an asset
_____	3. Payable	C. Right side of an account
_____	4. Journal	D. Side of an account where increases are recorded
_____	5. Receivable	E. Copying data from the journal to the ledger
_____	6. Capital	F. Increases in equity from providing goods and services
_____	7. Posting	G. Always a liability
_____	8. Revenue	H. Revenues – Expenses (where expenses exceed revenues)
_____	9. Net loss	I. Grouping of accounts
_____	10. Ledger	J. Owner's equity in the business

Starter 2–6 ②

For each of the following accounts, identify whether the normal balance is a debit or a credit:

a. Accounts Payable   _____

b. J. Yuen, Withdrawals   _____

c. Utilities Expense   _____

d. Cash   _____

e. Service Revenue   _____

f. Rent Expense   _____

g. Accounts Receivable   _____

Starter 2–8 ③

Lochlan Mystrie opened a wedding planning business. Record the following transactions in the journal of the business. Include an explanation with each journal entry.

Sep. 1   Mystrie invested $29,000 cash in a business bank account to start his business. The business received the cash and gave Mystrie owner's equity in the business.

     2   Purchased decorating supplies on account, $9,500.

     2   Paid cash for September's office rent of $4,100.

     3   Recorded $6,800 revenue for services rendered to clients on account.

Journal

DATE	ACCOUNT TITLES AND EXPLANATIONS	POST REF.	DEBIT	CREDIT

Starter 2-11 ③ ④

Nancy Carpenter Optical Dispensary bought supplies on account for $10,000 on September 8. On September 22, the company paid half on account.

1. Journalize the two transactions for Nancy Carpenter Optical Dispensary. Include an explanation for each transaction.
2. Open the Accounts Payable T-account and post to Accounts Payable. Compute the balance and denote it as *Bal*.

Requirement 1

		Journal			
DATE		ACCOUNT TITLES AND EXPLANATIONS	POST REF.	DEBIT	CREDIT

Requirement 2

Accounts Payable

Starter 2–13 ④

Calculate the account balance for each of the following T-accounts:

Accounts Receivable		Cash		Accounts Payable	
2,700	2,700	67,500	4,200	1,100	4,600
5,800	1,100	16,800	12,300		700
4,900	850				
	4,090				

Starter 2–15 ④ ⑤

Use the information shown below to prepare a trial balance for Balzy Indoor Tennis Club at November 30, 2017.

Balzy Indoor Tennis Club
General Ledger

Cash	10002	Furniture	17500	Accounts Payable	20001	Stan Balzy, Capital	30001
5,000	150	5,500		3,000	9,640		27,000
12,600	800			3,000	100		
955	475						
6,200	290						

Stan Balzy, Withdrawals	30002	Sales Revenue	40001	Supplies Expense	51200	Rent Expense	53200
1,200			5,500	2,500		4,000	

ACCT. NO.	ACCOUNT	DEBIT	CREDIT

Exercise 2–4 ②

For each of the following accounts, indicate the type of account and whether the normal balance of the account is a debit or a credit:

a. Interest Revenue   _____

b. Accounts Payable   _____

c. Chapman Li, Capital   _____

d. Office Supplies   _____

e. Advertising Expense   _____

f. Service Revenue   _____

g. Chapman Li, Withdrawals   _____

Exercise 2–5 ② ③

The following transactions occurred for London Engineering:

Jul. 2   Received $10,000 contribution from Bill London in exchange for capital.

       4   Paid utilities expense of $400.

       5   Purchased equipment on account for $2,100.

       10   Performed services for a client on account, $2,000.

       12   Borrowed $7,000 cash, signing a note payable.

       19   The owner, Bill London, withdrew $500 cash from the business.

       21   Purchased office supplies for $800 and paid cash.

       27   Paid the liability from July 5.

Required   Journalize the transactions of London Engineering. Include an explanation with each journal entry. Use the following accounts: Cash; Accounts Receivable; Office Supplies; Equipment; Accounts Payable; Notes Payable; B. London, Capital; B. London, Withdrawals; Service Revenue; Utilities Expense.

Journal

DATE		ACCOUNT TITLES AND EXPLANATIONS	POST REF.	DEBIT	CREDIT

Exercise 2–8 ③

Journalize the following transactions for DJ Services:

a. Owner, Liam Deresh, invested $2,500 cash into the business.
b. Rented a sound system and paid one month's rent, $1,100.
c. Performed DJ services on account, $1,700.
d. Paid $600 cash for equipment.
e. Owner, Liam Deresh, withdrew $500 cash for personal use.
f. Purchased $40 of supplies for cash.

		Journal			
DATE		ACCOUNT TITLES AND EXPLANATIONS	POST REF.	DEBIT	CREDIT

Exercise 2–12 ③ ④

Open the following three-column ledger accounts for Yarrow Strategic Consulting at May 1, 2017: Cash, #1100; Accounts Receivable, #1300; Office Supplies, #1500; Office Furniture, #1800; Accounts Payable, #2100; Florence Yarrow, Capital, #3100; Florence Yarrow, Withdrawals, #3200; Consulting Revenue, #4100; Rent Expense, #5500; Salary Expense, #5600.

Journalize the following May 2017 transactions on the ninth page of the journal, then post to the ledger accounts. Use the dates to identify the transactions.

May	2	Florence Yarrow opened a strategic consulting firm by investing $39,200 cash and office furniture valued at $16,200.
	2	Paid cash for May's rent of $2,500.
	2	Purchased office supplies on account, $1,800.
	15	Paid employee salary, $4,000 cash.
	17	Paid $1,200 of the account payable from May 2.
	19	Performed consulting service on account, $69,000.
	30	Withdrew $8,000 cash for personal use.

Journal					Page 9
DATE		ACCOUNT TITLES AND EXPLANATIONS	POST REF.	DEBIT	CREDIT

ACCOUNT	CASH				ACCOUNT NO. 1100
DATE		ITEM	JRNL. REF.	DEBIT	CREDIT	BALANCE

ACCOUNT	ACCOUNTS RECEIVABLE				ACCOUNT NO. 1300
DATE		ITEM	JRNL. REF.	DEBIT	CREDIT	BALANCE

ACCOUNT	OFFICE SUPPLIES				ACCOUNT NO. 1500
DATE		ITEM	JRNL. REF.	DEBIT	CREDIT	BALANCE

ACCOUNT	OFFICE FURNITURE				ACCOUNT NO. 1800
DATE		ITEM	JRNL. REF.	DEBIT	CREDIT	BALANCE

ACCOUNT	ACCOUNTS PAYABLE				ACCOUNT NO. 2100
DATE		ITEM	JRNL. REF.	DEBIT	CREDIT	BALANCE

ACCOUNT	FLORENCE YARROW, CAPITAL				ACCOUNT NO. 3100
DATE	ITEM	JRNL. REF.	DEBIT	CREDIT	BALANCE

ACCOUNT	FLORENCE YARROW, WITHDRAWALS				ACCOUNT NO. 3200
DATE	ITEM	JRNL. REF.	DEBIT	CREDIT	BALANCE

ACCOUNT	CONSULTING REVENUE				ACCOUNT NO. 4100
DATE	ITEM	JRNL. REF.	DEBIT	CREDIT	BALANCE

ACCOUNT	RENT EXPENSE				ACCOUNT NO. 5500
DATE	ITEM	JRNL. REF.	DEBIT	CREDIT	BALANCE

ACCOUNT	SALARY EXPENSE				ACCOUNT NO. 5600
DATE	ITEM	JRNL. REF.	DEBIT	CREDIT	BALANCE

40 Chapter 2

Exercise 2–16 ⑤

After recording the transactions in Exercise 2–12, prepare the unadjusted trial balance of Yarrow Strategic Consulting at May 31, 2017.

ACCT. NO.	ACCOUNT	DEBIT	CREDIT

Exercise 2–18 ② ③ ④ ⑤

Lee Management Consulting began operations and completed the following transactions during June 2016:

Jun.	2	Received $25,000 cash from owner Michael Lee. The business gave owner's equity in the business to Lee.
	2	Lee found a great downtown loft from which to operate. He paid cash for rent for the month of June, $3,000.
	3	Paid cash for a laptop, $1,000. The computer is expected to remain in service for four years. (Use the Equipment account for this transaction.)
	4	Purchased office furniture on account, $5,000. The furniture is expected to last for five years.
	5	Purchased supplies on account, $500.
	9	Performed consulting services for a client on account, $3,000.
	12	Paid utility expenses with cash, $250.
	18	Performed consulting services for a client and received cash of $2,000.
	21	Received $2,000 in advance for client services to be performed at a rate of $100 per day for a period of 20 days. (Use the liability account Unearned Revenue for this transaction. We will learn more about this account in Chapter 3.)
	22	Hired an office manager on a part-time basis. She will be paid $2,000 per month. She started work on Monday, June 25.
	23	Paid $500 cash for the account related to supplies purchased on June 5.
	26	Collected a partial payment of $1,500 from the consulting client invoiced on June 9.
	28	Michael Lee withdrew $2,000 cash for personal use.

Required

1. Open T-accounts in the ledger for Cash; Accounts Receivable; Supplies; Equipment; Furniture; Accounts Payable; Unearned Revenue; Michael Lee, Capital; Michael Lee, Withdrawals; Service Revenue; Rent Expense; Salaries Expense; and Utilities Expense.
2. Journalize the transactions. No explanations are required (to save time).
3. Post to the T-accounts. Identify all items by date and label an account balance as Bal. Formal posting references are not required.
4. Prepare an unadjusted trial balance at June 30, 2016.

Requirements 1 & 3

Cash

Accounts Receivable   Supplies

Requirements 1 & 3 (Continued)

Equipment	Furniture

Accounts Payable	Unearned Revenue

Michael Lee, Capital	Michael Lee, Withdrawals

Service Revenue	Rent Expense

Salaries Expense	Utilities Expense

Requirement 2

Journal					Page 1
DATE		ACCOUNT TITLES AND EXPLANATIONS	POST REF.	DEBIT	CREDIT

Requirement 4

ACCOUNT	DEBIT	CREDIT

Problem 2–2A ② ③

Zeb Slipewicz opened a renovation business called WeReDoIt Construction on September 3, 2017. During the first month of operations, the business completed the following transactions:

Sep.	3	Zeb deposited a cheque for $72,000 into the business bank account to start the business.
	4	Purchased supplies, $600, and furniture, $4,400, on account.
	5	Paid September rent expense, $1,500 cash.
	6	Performed design services for a client and received $2,400 cash.
	7	Paid $44,000 cash to acquire land for a future office site.
	10	Designed a bathroom for a client, billed the client, and received her promise to pay the $5,800 within one week.
	14	Paid for the furniture purchased September 4 on account.
	15	Paid assistant's salary, $940 cash.
	17	Received cash on account, $3,400.
	22	Received $5,000 cash from a client for renovation of a cottage.
	25	Prepared a recreation room design for a client on account, $1,600.
	30	Paid assistant's salary, $940 cash.
	30	Zeb withdrew $5,600 cash for personal use.

Required   Record each transaction in the journal with an explanation. Identify each transaction by date. Use the following accounts: Cash; Accounts Receivable; Supplies; Furniture; Land; Accounts Payable; Z. Slipewicz, Capital; Z. Slipewicz, Withdrawals; Service Revenue; Rent Expense; Salary Expense.

Journal
Page 1

DATE	ACCOUNT TITLES AND EXPLANATIONS	POST REF.	DEBIT	CREDIT

	Journal			Page 2
DATE	ACCOUNT TITLES AND EXPLANATIONS	POST REF.	DEBIT	CREDIT

Problem 2–3A ② ③ ④

The trial balance of Thomson Engineering at February 28, 2017, is shown below:

Account Number	Account	Debit	Credit
	THOMSON ENGINEERING		
	Trial Balance		
	February 28, 2017		
1100	Cash	$ 4,000	
1200	Accounts receivable	16,000	
1300	Supplies	3,600	
1600	Automobile	37,200	
2000	Accounts payable		$ 8,000
3000	R. Thomson, Capital		50,000
3100	R. Thomson, Withdrawals	4,400	
5000	Service revenue		16,400
6100	Rent expense	2,000	
6200	Salary expense	7,200	
	Total	$74,400	$74,400

During March, Thomson Engineering completed the following transactions:

Mar. 4   Collected $600 cash from a client on account.

8   Designed a system for a client on account, $580.

13   Paid cash for items purchased on account, $320.

18   Purchased supplies on account, $120.

20   R. Thomson withdrew $200 cash for personal use.

21   Received a verbal promise of a $2,000 contract.

22   Received cash of $620 for consulting work just completed.

31   Paid employees' salaries, $1,300 cash.

Required

1. Record the March transactions in Page 3 of the journal. Include an explanation for each entry.

2. Open three-column ledger accounts for the accounts listed in the trial balance, together with their balances at February 28. Enter Bal. (for previous balance) in the Item column, and place a check mark (✓) in the journal reference column for the February 28 balance in each account.

3. Post the transactions to the ledger, using dates, account numbers, journal references, and posting references.

Requirement 1

		Journal			Page 3
DATE		ACCOUNT TITLES AND EXPLANATIONS	POST REF.	DEBIT	CREDIT

Requirements 2 & 3

ACCOUNT: CASH					ACCOUNT NO. 1100	
DATE		ITEM	JRNL. REF.	DEBIT	CREDIT	BALANCE

ACCOUNT ACCOUNTS RECEIVABLE					ACCOUNT NO. 1200	
DATE		ITEM	JRNL. REF.	DEBIT	CREDIT	BALANCE

ACCOUNT SUPPLIES					ACCOUNT NO. 1300	
DATE		ITEM	JRNL. REF.	DEBIT	CREDIT	BALANCE

ACCOUNT AUTOMOBILE					ACCOUNT NO. 1600	
DATE		ITEM	JRNL. REF.	DEBIT	CREDIT	BALANCE

Requirements 2 & 3 (Continued)

ACCOUNT	ACCOUNTS PAYABLE				ACCOUNT NO. 2000
DATE	ITEM	JRNL. REF.	DEBIT	CREDIT	BALANCE

ACCOUNT	R. THOMSON, CAPITAL				ACCOUNT NO. 3000
DATE	ITEM	JRNL. REF.	DEBIT	CREDIT	BALANCE

ACCOUNT	R. THOMSON, WITHDRAWALS				ACCOUNT NO. 3100
DATE	ITEM	JRNL. REF.	DEBIT	CREDIT	BALANCE

ACCOUNT	SERVICE REVENUE				ACCOUNT NO. 5000
DATE	ITEM	JRNL. REF.	DEBIT	CREDIT	BALANCE

ACCOUNT	RENT EXPENSE				ACCOUNT NO. 6100
DATE	ITEM	JRNL. REF.	DEBIT	CREDIT	BALANCE

Requirements 2 & 3 (Continued)

ACCOUNT	SALARY EXPENSE					ACCOUNT NO. 6200
DATE	ITEM	JRNL. REF.	DEBIT	CREDIT	BALANCE	

Problem 2–4A ② ③ ④ ⑤

Sophie Vaillancourt started an investment management business, Vaillancourt Management, on June 1, 2017. During the first month of operations, the business completed the following selected transactions:

a. Sophie began the business with an investment of $20,000 cash, land valued at $60,000, and a building valued at $120,000. The business gave Sophie owner's equity in the business for the value of the cash, land, and building.

b. Purchased office supplies on account, $2,600.

c. Paid $15,000 cash for office furniture.

d. Paid employee salary, $2,200 cash.

e. Performed consulting service on account for clients, $12,100.

f. Paid in cash $800 of the account payable created in Transaction b.

g. Received a $2,000 bill for advertising expense that will be paid in the near future.

h. Performed consulting services for customers and received cash, $5,600.

i. Received cash on account, $2,400.

j. Paid the following cash expenses:
   (1) Rent of photocopier, $1,700.
   (2) Utilities, $400.

k. Sophie withdrew $6,500 cash for personal use.

Required

1. Record each transaction in the journal. Use the letters to identify the transactions.

2. Open the following three-column ledger accounts: Cash, #1100; Accounts Receivable, #1300; Office Supplies, #1400; Office Furniture, #1500; Building, #1700; Land, #1800; Accounts Payable, #2100; Sophie Vaillancourt, Capital, #3100; Sophie Vaillancourt, Withdrawals, #3200; Service Revenue, #4100; Advertising Expense, #5100; Equipment Rental Expense, #5300; Salary Expense, #5500; Utilities Expense, #5700.

3. Post to the accounts and keep a running balance for each account.

4. Prepare the unadjusted trial balance of Vaillancourt Management at June 30, 2017.

Requirement 1

Journal

DATE		ACCOUNT TITLES AND EXPLANATIONS	POST REF.	DEBIT	CREDIT

Requirement 1 (Continued)

Journal					
DATE		ACCOUNT TITLES AND EXPLANATIONS	POST REF.	DEBIT	CREDIT

Requirements 2 & 3

ACCOUNT	CASH				ACCOUNT NO. 1100
DATE (letter)		ITEM	JRNL. REF.	DEBIT	CREDIT	BALANCE

ACCOUNT	ACCOUNTS RECEIVABLE				ACCOUNT NO. 1300
DATE (letter)		ITEM	JRNL. REF.	DEBIT	CREDIT	BALANCE

ACCOUNT	OFFICE SUPPLIES				ACCOUNT NO. 1400
DATE (letter)		ITEM	JRNL. REF.	DEBIT	CREDIT	BALANCE

ACCOUNT	OFFICE FURNITURE				ACCOUNT NO. 1500
DATE (letter)		ITEM	JRNL. REF.	DEBIT	CREDIT	BALANCE

Requirements 2 & 3 (Continued)

ACCOUNT BUILDING					ACCOUNT NO. 1700
DATE (letter)	ITEM	JRNL. REF.	DEBIT	CREDIT	BALANCE

ACCOUNT LAND					ACCOUNT NO. 1800
DATE (letter)	ITEM	JRNL. REF.	DEBIT	CREDIT	BALANCE

ACCOUNT ACCOUNTS PAYABLE					ACCOUNT NO. 2100
DATE (letter)	ITEM	JRNL. REF.	DEBIT	CREDIT	BALANCE

ACCOUNT SOPHIE VAILLANCOURT, CAPITAL					ACCOUNT NO. 3100
DATE (letter)	ITEM	JRNL. REF.	DEBIT	CREDIT	BALANCE

ACCOUNT SOPHIE VAILLANCOURT, WITHDRAWALS					ACCOUNT NO. 3200
DATE (letter)	ITEM	JRNL. REF.	DEBIT	CREDIT	BALANCE

Requirements 2 & 3 (Continued)

ACCOUNT	SERVICE REVENUE				ACCOUNT NO. 4100
DATE (letter)	ITEM	JRNL. REF.	DEBIT	CREDIT	BALANCE

ACCOUNT	ADVERTISING EXPENSE				ACCOUNT NO. 5100
DATE (letter)	ITEM	JRNL. REF.	DEBIT	CREDIT	BALANCE

ACCOUNT	EQUIPMENT RENTAL EXPENSE				ACCOUNT NO. 5300
DATE (letter)	ITEM	JRNL. REF.	DEBIT	CREDIT	BALANCE

ACCOUNT	SALARY EXPENSE				ACCOUNT NO. 5500
DATE (letter)	ITEM	JRNL. REF.	DEBIT	CREDIT	BALANCE

ACCOUNT	UTILITIES EXPENSE				ACCOUNT NO. 5700
DATE (letter)	ITEM	JRNL. REF.	DEBIT	CREDIT	BALANCE

Requirement 4

ACCT. NO.	ACCOUNT	DEBIT	CREDIT

Problem 2–6A ② ⑤

The following trial balance does not balance:

MINTER LANDSCAPE CONSULTING		
Trial Balance		
June 30, 2017		
Cash	$ 1,600	
Accounts receivable	10,000	
Supplies	900	
Office furniture	3,600	
Land	46,600	
Accounts payable		$ 3,800
Notes payable		23,000
R. Minter, capital		31,600
R. Minter, withdrawals	2,000	
Consulting service revenue		7,300
Advertising expense	400	
Rent expense	1,000	
Salary expense	2,100	
Utilities expense	410	
Total	$68,610	$65,700

The following errors were detected:

a. The cash balance is understated by $1,300.

b. The cost of the land was $44,600, not $46,600.

c. A $400 purchase of supplies on account was neither journalized nor posted.

d. A $3,000 credit to Consulting Service Revenue was not posted.

e. Rent Expense of $200 was posted as a credit rather than a debit.

f. The balance of Advertising Expense is $600, but it was listed as $400 on the trial balance.

g. A $300 debit to Accounts Receivable was posted as $30. The credit to Consulting Service Revenue was correct.

h. The balance of Utilities Expense is overstated by $80.

i. A $900 debit to the R. Minter, Withdrawals account was posted as a debit to R. Minter, Capital.

Required   Prepare the corrected trial balance at June 30, 2017. Journal entries are not required.

ACCOUNT	DEBIT	CREDIT

Calculations:

Problem 2–7A ② ③ ④ ⑤

CrossCountry Movers had the following account balances, in random order, on December 15, 2017 (all accounts have their "normal" balances):

Moving fees income....................	$261,600	Cash..	$ 17,200
Accounts receivable....................	17,400	Storage fees income.................	57,900
Rent expense................................	47,100	Notes receivable.......................	45,000
H. Martinez, capital....................	63,000	Utilities expense.......................	2,400
Office supplies expense.............	2,100	Office supplies.........................	9,600
Mortgage payable.......................	39,000	Accounts payable.....................	33,000
Salaries expense..........................	161,100	Office equipment......................	12,300
Insurance expense......................	6,300	Moving equipment...................	132,200

The following events took place during the final weeks of the year:

Dec. 16   The accountant discovered that an error had been made in posting an entry to the Moving Fees Income account. The entry was correctly journalized, but $2,400 was accidentally posted as $4,200 in the account.

17   Moved a customer's goods to CrossCountry's rented warehouse for storage. The moving fees were $4,000. Storage fees are $600 per month. The customer was billed for one month's storage and the moving fees.

18   Collected a $15,000 note owed to CrossCountry Movers and collected interest income of $1,800 cash.

19   Used a company cheque to pay for Martinez's hydro bill in the amount of $400.

21   Purchased storage racks for $12,000. Paid $3,600 cash, provided moving services for $1,500, and promised to pay the balance in 60 days.

23   Collected $3,000 cash; $2,600 of this was for moving goods on December 15 (recorded as an account receivable at that time) and the balance was for storage fees for the period of December 16 to 23.

24   CrossCountry Movers paid cash of $18,000 owing on the mortgage.

27   Martinez withdrew $5,000 cash for personal use.

29   Provided moving services to a lawyer for $2,400. The lawyer paid CrossCountry Movers $1,500 and provided legal work for the balance.

31   Martinez, the owner of CrossCountry Movers, sold 2,000 shares he held in Brandon Haulage Inc. for $12,000.

Required

1. Where appropriate, record each transaction from December 16 to 31 in the journal. Include an explanation for each journal entry.
2. Post entries in T-accounts and calculate the balance of each one.
3. Prepare the unadjusted trial balance of CrossCountry Movers at December 31, 2017.

Requirement 1

	Journal			
DATE	ACCOUNT TITLES AND EXPLANATIONS	POST REF.	DEBIT	CREDIT

Requirement 1 (Continued)

DATE		ACCOUNT TITLES AND EXPLANATIONS	POST REF.	DEBIT	CREDIT

Table heading: Journal

Requirement 2

Cash		Accounts Receivable

Notes Receivable		Office Supplies

Office Equipment		Moving Equipment

Storage Equipment		Accounts Payable

Mortgage Payable		H. Martinez, Capital

Requirement 2 (Continued)

H. Martinez, Withdrawals

Moving Fees Income

Storage Fees Income

Interest Income

Insurance Expense

Legal Expense

Office Supplies Expense

Rent Expense

Salaries Expense

Utilities Expense

Requirement 3

ACCOUNT	DEBIT	CREDIT

Extra Journal Paper

DATE		ACCOUNTS TITLES AND EXPLANATIONS	POST REF.	DEBIT	CREDIT

3 MEASURING BUSINESS INCOME: THE ADJUSTING PROCESS

LEARNING OBJECTIVES

1 Apply the recognition criteria for revenues and expenses.
2 Distinguish accrual-basis accounting from cash-basis accounting.
3 Prepare adjusting entries.
4 Prepare an adjusted trial balance.
5 Prepare the financial statements from the adjusted trial balance.
6 Describe the adjusting-process implications of International Financial Reporting Standards (IFRS).

*A1 Account for a prepaid expense recorded initially as an expense.
*A2 Account for an unearned (deferred) revenue recorded initially as a revenue.

Starter 3–4 ②

Suppose you work summers house-sitting for people while they are away on vacation. Most of your customers pay you immediately after you finish a job. A few ask you to send them a bill. It is now June 30 and you have collected $600 from cash-paying customers. Your remaining customers owe you $1,400. How much service revenue would you have under the (a) cash basis and (b) accrual basis of accounting? Which method of accounting provides more information about your house-sitting business? Explain your answer.

a. and b.

_____

_____

_____

_____

_____

_____

_____

_____

Starter 3–14 ④

Scott Tax Services had the following accounts and account balances after adjusting entries. Assume all accounts have normal balances. Prepare the adjusted trial balance for Scott Tax Services' year end of September 30, 2017.

Cash..	$18,150	Equipment...	$15,000
Land...	20,000	Accounts Receivable...	2,250
Utilities Payable...	350	Office Supplies...	200
Accounts Payable...	3,100	S. Scott, Capital...	18,400
Accumulated Amortization—Equipment.........	2,400	Utilities Expense...	750
Service Revenue...	60,000	Unearned Revenue..	600
Supplies Expense..	800	Amortization Expense—Equipment...................	1,200
S. Scott, Withdrawals...	22,000	Salaries Expense..	4,500

ACCOUNT	DEBIT	CREDIT

Starter 3–17 ⑥

Do International Financial Reporting Standards (IFRS) for publicly accountable enterprises in Canada have an impact on the adjusting process for these companies?

_____

_____

_____

_____

_____

_____

_____

_____

_____

_____

_____

*Starter 3–18 Ⓐ①

On June 30, 2017, Magnus' Muffins paid $18,000 for business insurance for the next year. Record the entries for the purchase of the insurance by recording it as an expense and then making a year-end entry on December 31, 2017, to adjust the accounts.

	Journal			
DATE	ACCOUNT TITLES AND EXPLANATIONS	POST REF.	DEBIT	CREDIT

*Starter 3–19 (A2)

On November 1, 2017, Freya Albatter's orthodontic office received a $2,500 prepayment from a client for dental work to be performed on November 22. The appointment got postponed until January 15, 2018. Prepare the journal entries for November 1, the December 31 year end, and the January 15 appointment dates. Assume that the prepayment was recorded as a revenue because, at that time, it was assumed the work would be performed within the month.

Journal

DATE		ACCOUNT TITLES AND EXPLANATIONS	POST REF.	DEBIT	CREDIT

Exercise 3–2 (1)

Dominion Storage operates approximately 300 mini-warehouses across Canada. The company's headquarters are in Medicine Hat, Alberta. During 2017, Dominion earned rental revenue of $26.0 million and collected cash of $23.6 million from customers. Total expenses for 2017 were $17.4 million, of which Dominion paid $15.9 million.

Required

1. Apply the recognition criteria for revenues and the matching objective to compute Dominion Storage's net income for 2017.
2. Identify the information that you did not use to compute Dominion Storage's net income. Give the reason for not using the information.

Requirements 1 & 2

_____

_____

_____

_____

_____

_____

_____

Exercise 3–5 ③

Compute the missing amounts and insert them in the shaded areas for each of the following Prepaid Insurance situations. For situations A and B, make the needed journal entry. Consider each situation separately.

Situations

	A	B	C	D	E
Beginning Prepaid Insurance	$ 4,200	$ 5,000	$16,800	$5,900	
Payments for Prepaid Insurance during the year	19,800		15,000		2,500
Total amount to account for			31,800	15,600	
Ending Prepaid Insurance	19,000	6,000		6,000	1,400
Insurance Expense		$12,000	$25,000	$9,600	$2,600

Journal entries for A and B

	Journal				
DATE	ACCOUNTS TITLES AND EXPLANATIONS	POST REF.	DEBIT	CREDIT	

Calculations:

Exercise 3–9 ③

Journalize the adjusting entry needed at December 31 for each of the following independent situations:

a. On June 1, when we collected $48,000 rent in advance, we debited Cash and credited Unearned Rent Revenue. The tenant was paying for one year's rent in advance. At December 31, we must account for the amount of rent we have earned.

b. Interest revenue of $2,400 has been earned but not yet received on a $60,000 note receivable held by the business.

c. Salaries expense is $7,500 per day—Monday through Friday—and the business pays employees each Friday. This year December 31 falls on a Wednesday.

d. Equipment was purchased last year at a cost of $200,000. The equipment's useful life is five years. It will have no value after five years. Record the year's amortization.

e. On September 1, when we paid $6,000 for a one-year insurance policy, we debited Prepaid Insurance and credited Cash.

f. The business owes interest expense of $7,200 that it will pay early in the next period.

g. The unadjusted balance of the Supplies account is $13,500. The total cost of supplies remaining on hand on December 31 is $4,500.

a. – g.

	Journal			
DATE	ACCOUNT TITLES AND EXPLANATIONS	POST REF.	DEBIT	CREDIT

Exercise 3–10 ③

Journalize the following December 31 transactions for College Park Printing Services. No explanations are required.

a. Equipment cost $24,000 and is expected to be useful for 10 years, at which time it will have no residual value. Calculate and record amortization for the current year.

b. Each Monday, College Park pays employees for the previous week's work. The amount of weekly payroll is $5,600 for a seven-day workweek (Monday to Sunday). This year December 31 falls on a Thursday.

c. The beginning balance of Supplies was $2,500. During the year, College Park purchased supplies for $3,000, and at December 31 the supplies on hand totalled $1,700.

d. College Park prepaid one year of insurance coverage on August 1 of the current year, $5,280. Record insurance expense for the year ended December 31.

e. College Park earned $3,200 of unearned revenue.

f. College Park incurred $150 of interest expense on a note payable that will not be paid until February 28.

g. College Park billed customers $6,000 for printing services performed.

	Journal				
DATE	ACCOUNT TITLES AND EXPLANATIONS	POST REF.	DEBIT	CREDIT	

Calculations:

Exercise 3–11   ③

For each of the following independent situations, journalize both the initial transaction and the subsequent adjusting entry:

a. Dec. 1   – business receives $2,000 for a 10-month service contract.
    Dec. 31 – year-end adjusting entry needed to update the balance in the account.

b. Mar. 31 – work performed but not yet billed to customers for the month, $900.
    Apr. 21 – received payment for the work that was completed.

c. Jun. 15 – purchased $3,500 of office supplies on account.
    Dec. 31 – a count of supplies shows that only $1,700 worth is left at year end, so the balance in the account needs to be updated.

d. Feb. 2   – business paid a $450 deposit for the last month's rental of a copier on a 10-month contract.
    Nov. 30 – the rental period for the copier ended, so the balance in the prepaid account must be updated.

Journal					
DATE	ACCOUNT TITLES AND EXPLANATIONS	POST REF.	DEBIT	CREDIT	

Journal

DATE		ACCOUNT TITLES AND EXPLANATIONS	POST REF.	DEBIT	CREDIT

Calculations:

Exercise 3–15 ④

Prepare an adjusted trial balance for Nature Valley Cleaners as at June 30, 2017. Assume that all accounts have their normal balances.

Accounts payable	$4,000
Accumulated amortization—equipment	7,000
Amortization expense—equipment	1,000
Cash	2,400
Equipment	40,000
Insurance expense	200
Les Valley, capital	17,000
Les Valley, withdrawals	8,000
Prepaid insurance	1,800
Salaries expense	16,000
Salaries payable	2,000
Service revenue	44,000
Supplies	4,000
Supplies expense	2,000
Unearned service revenue	1,400

ACCOUNT	DEBIT	CREDIT

Exercise 3–17 ⑤

Refer to the data in Exercise 3-15. Prepare Nature Valley Cleaners' income statement and statement of owner's equity for the year ended June 30, 2017. Then prepare the balance sheet on that date.

Exercise 3–22 ③ ④ ⑤

Refer to Exercise 2–18 of Chapter 2. Start from the unadjusted trial balance and the posted T-accounts that Lee Management Consulting prepared at June 30. Make sure the account balances in your trial balance and T-accounts match those in the trial balance at June 30, 2016.

LEE MANAGEMENT CONSULTING		
Unadjusted Trial Balance		
June 30, 2016		
	Debits	Credits
Cash	$23,750	
Accounts receivable	1,500	
Supplies	500	
Equipment	1,000	
Furniture	5,000	
Accounts payable		$ 5,000
Unearned revenue		2,000
Michael Lee, capital		25,000
Michael Lee, withdrawals	2,000	
Service revenue		5,000
Rent expense	3,000	
Utilities expense	250	
Total	$37,000	$37,000

At June 30, the company gathers the following information for the adjusting entries:

a. Accrued service revenue, $400.

b. Earned $800 of the service revenue collected in advance on June 21 for eight days of work.

c. Supplies remaining on hand at June 30, $100.

d. Amortization expense—equipment, $42; furniture, $167 (all amounts are rounded to the nearest dollar).

e. Accrued $500 expense for the secretary's salary.

Required

1. Open these new T-accounts: Accumulated Amortization—Equipment; Accumulated Amortization—Furniture; Salaries Payable; Amortization Expense—Equipment; Amortization Expense—Furniture; Salaries Expense; Supplies Expense.

2. Journalize each of the entries.

3. Post the adjusting entries into the T-accounts. Label each adjusting amount as *Adj.* and an account balance as *Bal.*

4. Prepare an adjusted trial balance at June 30, 2016. List expenses in alphabetical order.

5. Prepare the income statement and statement of owner's equity of Lee Management Consulting for the month ended June 30, 2016, then prepare the balance sheet at that date. (Hint: List the expenses in alphabetical order.)

Requirements 1 & 3

Cash		Accounts Receivable	

Supplies		Equipment	

Accumulated Amortization—Equipment		Furniture	

Accumulated Amortization—Furniture		Accounts Payable	

Salaries Payable		Unearned Revenue	

Requirements 1 & 3 (Continued)

Michael Lee, Capital

Michael Lee, Withdrawals

Service Revenue

Amortization Expense—Equipment

Amortization Expense—Furniture

Rent Expense

Salaries Expense

Supplies Expense

Utilities Expense

Journal

DATE		ACCOUNTS TITLES AND EXPLANATIONS	POST REF.	DEBIT	CREDIT

Requirement 4

ACCOUNT	DEBIT	CREDIT

Requirement 5

Problem 3–3A ③

Journalize the adjusting entry needed on December 31, the company's year end, for each of the following independent cases affecting Eagle Communications:

a. Each Friday the company pays its employees for the current week's work. The amount of the payroll is $15,000 for a five-day workweek. The current accounting period ends on Wednesday.

b. Eagle has received notes receivable from some clients for professional services. During the current year, Eagle has earned interest revenue of $800, which will be received next year.

c. The beginning balance of Supplies was $4,800. During the year the company purchased supplies costing $7,600, and at December 31 the inventory of supplies remaining on hand is $3,200.

d. The company is developing a wireless communication system for a large company, and the client paid Eagle $120,000 at the start of the project. Eagle recorded this amount as Unearned Consulting Revenue. The development will take several months to complete. Eagle executives estimate that the company has earned three-fourths of the total fee during the current year.

e. Amortization for the current year includes the following: Office Furniture, $8,600, and Design Equipment, $16,000. Make a compound entry. (Hint: This means showing everything in one journal entry and not two.)

f. Details of Prepaid Insurance are shown in the account:

Prepaid Insurance	
Jan. 2 Bal.	6,000

Eagle Communications prepays a full year's insurance on January 2. Record insurance expense for the year ended December 31 as one annual adjustment for what was used for the year.

Calculations:

a. – f.

DATE		ACCOUNTS TITLES AND EXPLANATIONS	POST REF.	DEBIT	CREDIT

Journal

Problem 3–4A ③

Laughter Landscaping has collected the following data for the December 31 adjusting entries:

a. Each Friday, Laughter pays employees for the current week's work. The amount of the weekly payroll is $7,000 for a five-day workweek. This year December 31 falls on a Wednesday. Laughter will pay its employees on January 2.

b. On January 1 of the current year, Laughter purchased an insurance policy that covers two years, $9,000.

c. The beginning balance of Office Supplies was $4,000. During the year, Laughter purchased office supplies for $5,200, and at December 31 the office supplies on hand total $2,400.

d. During December, Laughter designed a landscape plan and the client prepaid $7,000. Laughter recorded this amount as Unearned Revenue. The job will take two months to complete. Laughter estimates that the company has earned 75 percent of the total revenue in the current year and will finish by January 12.

e. At December 31, Laughter had earned $3,500 for landscape services completed for Turnkey Appliances. Turnkey has stated that they will pay Laughter on January 10.

f. Amortization for the current year includes Equipment, $3,700, and Trucks, $1,300. Make one compound entry to record the amortization, but use separate amortization accounts for each asset.

g. Laughter has incurred $300 of interest expense on a $450 interest payment due on January 15.

Required

1. Journalize the adjusting entry needed on December 31 for each of the previous items affecting Laughter Landscaping. Assume Laughter records adjusting entries only at the end of the year.

2. Journalize the subsequent journal entries for adjusting entries a, d, and g.

Requirement 1

DATE	ACCOUNT TITLES AND EXPLANATIONS	POST REF.	DEBIT	CREDIT

88 Chapter 3

Requirements 1 & 2

	Journal			
DATE	ACCOUNT TITLES AND EXPLANATIONS	POST REF.	DEBIT	CREDIT

Problem 3-7A ③④⑤

Consider the unadjusted trial balance of Burrows Landscaping at December 31, 2017, and the related month-end adjustment data:

BURROWS LANDSCAPING		
Unadjusted Trial Balance		
December 31, 2017		
Cash	$ 24,500	
Accounts receivable	22,000	
Prepaid rent	9,000	
Supplies	5,500	
Equipment	66,000	
Accumulated amortization—equipment		$ 12,650
Accounts payable		7,200
Salaries payable		0
A. Burrows, capital		122,700
A. Burrows, withdrawals	25,000	
Landscaping design revenue		126,000
Salaries expense	82,000	
Rent expense	22,500	
Utilities expense	6,000	
Amortization expense—equipment	6,050	
Supplies expense	0	
Total	$268,550	$268,550

The following adjustments need to be made before the financial statements for the year can be prepared:

a. Accrued landscaping design revenue at December 31, $8,500.

b. One month of the prepaid rent had been used. The unadjusted prepaid balance of $9,000 relates to the four-month period December 1, 2017, through March 31, 2018.

c. Supplies remaining on hand at December 31, $900.

d. Amortization on equipment for the month of December. The equipment's expected useful life is 10 years; it will have no value at the end of its useful life, and the straight-line method of amortization is used.

e. Accrued salaries expense at December 31 should be for two days only. The five-day weekly payroll is $10,000.

Required

1. Sketch T-accounts in your notes to calculate the new balances. Prepare the adjusted trial balance of Burrows Landscaping at December 31, 2017.

2. Prepare the income statement (record expenses from largest to smallest on the income statement) and the statement of owner's equity for the year ended December 31, 2017, and the balance sheet at December 31, 2017. Draw the arrows linking the three financial statements, or write a short description of how they are linked.

Requirement 1

Cash

Accounts Receivable

Prepaid Rent

Supplies

Equipment

Accumulated Amortization—Equipment

Accounts Payable

Salaries Payable

Requirement 1 (Continued)

A. Burrows, Capital		A. Burrows, Withdrawals

Landscaping Design Revenue		Salaries Expense

Rent Expense		Utilities Expense

Amortization Expense-Equipment		Supplies Expense

Requirement 1 (Continued)

ACCOUNT	DEBIT	CREDIT

Calculations:

Requirement 2

Problem 3–8A ③ ④ ⑤

Pace Employment Counsellors provides counselling services to employees of companies that are downsizing. The business had the following account balances:

PACE EMPLOYMENT COUNSELLORS		
Unadjusted Trial Balance		
December 1, 2017		
Cash	$ 19,000	
Accounts receivable	23,200	
Prepaid advertising	1,500	
Supplies	5,000	
Computer equipment	69,000	
Accumulated amortization—computer equipment		$ 0
Building	288,000	
Accumulated amortization—building		0
Land	144,000	
Accounts payable		93,600
B. Pace, capital		330,000
B. Pace, withdrawals	79,000	
Counselling revenue		342,500
Salaries expense	120,000	
Supplies expense	0	
Utilities expense	17,400	
Total	$766,100	$766,100

The following transactions occurred during December:

a. On December 1, paid cash to a marketing firm for four months of advertising work in advance. The contract was for $2,875 per month.

b. On December 6, supplies in the amount of $3,700 were purchased on account.

c. On December 15, the company received a cash advance of $8,000 for work to be performed starting January 1, 2018.

d. On December 29, the company provided counselling services to a customer for $15,000, to be paid in 30 days.

The following information was available on December 31, 2017:

e. A physical count shows $7,600 of supplies remaining on hand on December 31.

f. The building has an expected useful life of eight years with no expected value after eight years. The building was purchased on January 2, and the straight-line method of amortization is used.

g. The computer equipment, purchased on January 2, is expected to be used for four years with no expected value after four years. The straight-line method of amortization is used.

h. The marketing firm has performed one-quarter of the work on the contract.

i. The company's managing director, who earns $800 per day, worked the last six days of the year and will be paid on January 4, 2018.

Required

1. Journalize the entries. Add new accounts if necessary.

2. Prepare an adjusted trial balance on December 31, 2017.

3. Prepare an income statement for the year ended December 31, 2017. List expenses in the order of dollar amount, from the greatest amount to the smallest.

4. Prepare a statement of owner's equity for the year ended December 31, 2017. Assume there have been no changes to the capital account since January 1.

5. Prepare a balance sheet at December 31, 2017.

Requirement 1

	Journal			
DATE	ACCOUNT TITLES AND EXPLANATIONS	POST REF.	DEBIT	CREDIT

Requirement 2

ACCOUNT	DEBIT	CREDIT

Optional

Cash	
Bal.	19,000	

Accounts Receivable	
Bal.	23,200	

Prepaid Advertising	
Bal.	1,500	

Supplies	
Bal.	5,000	

Computer Equipment	
Bal.	69,000	

Accumulated Amortization—Computer Equipment

Building	
Bal.	288,000	

Accumulated Amortization—Building

Optional (Continued)

Land	
Bal. 144,000	

Accounts Payable	
	Bal. 93,600

B. Pace, Capital	
	Bal. 330,000

B. Pace, Withdrawals	
Bal. 79,000	

Counselling Revenue	
	Bal. 342,500

Salaries Expense	
Bal. 120,000	

Supplies Expense	

Utilities Expense	
Bal. 17,400	

Requirements 3 – 5

Extra Journal Paper

DATE		ACCOUNTS TITLES AND EXPLANATIONS	POST REF.	DEBIT	CREDIT

4 COMPLETING THE ACCOUNTING CYCLE

LEARNING OBJECTIVES

1 Prepare an accounting worksheet.
2 Complete the accounting cycle.
3 Close the revenue, expense, and withdrawal accounts.
4 Correct typical accounting errors.
5 Classify assets and liabilities as current or long term, and prepare a classified balance sheet.
6 Use the current ratio and the debt ratio to evaluate a company.
7 Describe the accounting cycle and financial reporting implications of International Financial Reporting Standards (IFRS).

*A1 Describe and prepare reversing entries.

Starter 4–1 ①

Scissors Hair Stylists has begun the preparation of its adjusted trial balance as follows:

SCISSORS HAIR STYLISTS
Preparation of Adjusted Trial Balance
December 31, 2017

ACCOUNT TITLE	UNADJUSTED TRIAL BALANCE DEBIT	CREDIT	ADJUSTMENTS DEBIT	CREDIT	ADJUSTED TRIAL BALANCE DEBIT	CREDIT
Cash	600					
Supplies	800					
Equipment	16,200					
Accumulated amortization—equipment		1,100				
Accounts payable		500				
Interest payable		0				
Note payable		2,900				
Suzanne Byrd, capital		5,300				
Service revenue		13,000				
Rent expense	4,800					
Supplies expense	0					
Amortization expense	0					
Interest expense	400					
	22,800	22,800				

Year-end data:

a. Supplies remaining on hand, $300

b. Amortization, $1,100

c. Accrued interest expense, $700

Complete the company's adjusted trial balance. Identify each adjustment by its letter. You may write your answer in the spaces provided on the adjusted trial balance.

Starter 4–3 ①

1. Does this portion of the worksheet show a net income or a net loss? What is the amount of the net income or the net loss?

Income Statement		Balance Sheet	
Dr	Cr	Dr	Cr
150,000	120,000	650,850	680,850
	30,000	30,000	
150,000	150,000	680,850	680,850

_____

_____

2. Complete this portion of the worksheet. What is the amount of the net income or the net loss?

Income Statement		Balance Sheet	
Dr	Cr	Dr	Cr
194,000	223,500	416,800	387,300

Starter 4–13 ④

Suppose a company made the following journal entry to pay for supplies purchased:

Mar. 31	Accounts Receivable	200	
	Cash		200
	To pay for supplies purchased on account.		

Is this an error? If so, correct the error using both methods shown in this chapter. Provide an explanation for each journal entry.

Journal

DATE		ACCOUNT TITLES AND EXPLANATIONS	POST REF.	DEBIT	CREDIT

Starter 4–16 ⑤

Indicate where each of the following accounts would be reported in the financial statements for the year ended December 31, 2016:

1. _____ Prepaid Rent
2. _____ Unearned Revenue
3. _____ Note Payable (due June 30, 2019)
4. _____ Accounts Receivable
5. _____ Accounts Payable
6. _____ Accumulated Amortization
7. _____ Supplies
8. _____ Company Truck

a. Property, plant, and equipment
b. Current asset
c. Current liability
d. Long-term liability

Starter 4–19 ⑥

Daleyza Racing has these account balances at December 31, 2017:

Accounts Payable	$ 8,700	Note Payable, Long-term	$18,000
Accounts Receivable	12,500	Prepaid Rent	4,000
Cash	6,500	Salaries Payable	4,200
Accum. Amortization—Equipment	8,000	Service Revenue	62,000
Equipment	24,000	Supplies	3,000

Compute Daleyza Racing's current ratio and debt ratio.

Current ratio:

Debt ratio:

Starter 4–21 ⑦

Answer the following questions about IFRS:

1. What are the two main options (those illustrated in the chapter) for balance sheet presentation for companies following IFRS?
2. Explain what is meant by the term "reverse order of liquidity."
3. What is another name for a balance sheet that may be used by corporations reporting under IFRS?

1. – 3.

_____

_____

_____

_____

_____

_____

_____

_____

_____

_____

_____

_____

_____

Exercise 4–1 ①

The unadjusted trial balance of Overland Trekkers appears below:

OVERLAND TREKKERS				
Worksheet				
September 30, 2017				
	UNADJUSTED TRIAL BALANCE		**ADJUSTMENTS**	
ACCOUNT TITLE	**DEBIT**	**CREDIT**	**DEBIT**	**CREDIT**
Cash	14,240			
Accounts receivable	11,880			
Prepaid rent	2,400			
Supplies	6,780			
Equipment	65,200			
Accum. amortization—equipment		5,680		
Accounts payable		10,320		
Salaries payable		0		
R. Puri, capital		72,060		
R. Puri, withdrawals	6,000			
Service revenue		23,600		
Amortization expense—equipment	0			
Salaries expense	3,600			
Rent expense	0			
Utilities expense	1,560			
Supplies expense	0			
	111,660	111,660		

Additional information at September 30, 2017:

a. The business had sales that were not recorded yet in the amount of $840. It must accrue this service revenue.

b. Equipment amortization in the amount of $260 needs to be recorded.

c. The business needs to accrue salaries expense of $2,100 for work done but not yet recorded.

d. Prepaid rent used in the amount of $1,200.

e. Supplies worth $3,200 were used up during the period.

Required Complete the Overland Trekkers worksheet for September 2017. What was net income for the month ended September 30, 2017?

OVERLAND TREKKERS					
Worksheet					
September 30, 2017					
ADJUSTED TRIAL BALANCE		INCOME STATEMENT		BALANCE SHEET	
DEBIT	CREDIT	DEBIT	CREDIT	DEBIT	CREDIT

Exercise 4–2 ③

Journalize the adjusting and closing entries for the company in Exercise 4–1. Include explanations.

Journal

DATE	ACCOUNT TITLES AND EXPLANATIONS	POST REF.	DEBIT	CREDIT

Exercise 4–3   ③

Set up T-accounts for only those accounts affected by the adjusting and closing entries in Exercise 4–1. Post the adjusting and closing entries from Exercise 4–2 to the accounts, identifying adjustment amounts as *Adj.*, closing amounts as *Clo.*, and balances as *Bal.* Double underline the accounts with zero balances after you close them and show the ending balance in each account.

Accounts Receivable			
Bal.	11,880		

Prepaid Rent			
Bal.	2,400		

Supplies			
Bal.	6,780		

Accumulated Amortization—Equipment			
		Bal.	5,680

Salaries Payable			

R. Puri, Capital			
		Bal.	72,060

R. Puri, Withdrawals			
Bal.	6,000		

Income Summary			

Service Revenue		
	Bal.	23,600

Amortization Expense—Equipment		

Rent Expense		

Salaries Expense		
Bal.	3,600	

Supplies Expense		

Utilities Expense		
Bal.	1,560	

Exercise 4–4 ③

After completing Exercises 4–2 and 4–3, prepare the post-closing trial balance for Overland Trekkers at September 30, 2017.

OVERLAND TREKKERS		
Post-Closing Trial Balance		
September 30, 2017		
ACCOUNT	DEBIT	CREDIT
Cash		
Accounts receivable		
Prepaid rent		
Supplies		
Equipment		
Accumulated amortization—equipment		
Accounts payable		
Salaries payable		
R. Puri, capital		
Total		

Exercise 4–8 ③

The adjusted trial balance for Paddy's Cell Systems follows:

PADDY'S CELL SYSTEMS		
Adjusted Trial Balance		
March 31, 2017		
Cash	$ 27,600	
Supplies	7,500	
Prepaid rent	3,600	
Office equipment	168,900	
Accumulated amortization—office equipment		$ 26,050
Accounts payable		29,300
Salaries payable		3,250
Unearned service revenue		17,600
P. O'Neill, capital		153,300
P. O'Neill, withdrawals	15,000	
Service revenue		61,000
Salaries expense	45,200	
Rent expense	15,650	
Amortization expense—office equipment	1,200	
Supplies expense	2,650	
Utilities expense	3,200	
	$290,500	$290,500

Required

1. Journalize the closing entries of Paddy's Cell Systems at March 31, 2017. Include explanations.
2. How much net income or net loss did Paddy's Cell Systems earn for March 2017? How can you tell?

Requirement 1

		Journal			
DATE		ACCOUNT TITLES AND EXPLANATIONS	POST REF.	DEBIT	CREDIT

Requirement 2

Exercise 4–10 ④

Prepare a correcting entry (or entries), with explanations, for each of the following accounting errors:

a. Debited Supplies and credited Accounts Payable for a $9,000 purchase of office equipment on account.

b. Accrued interest revenue of $3,000 by a debit to Accounts Receivable and a credit to Interest Revenue.

c. Adjusted prepaid rent by debiting Prepaid Rent and crediting Rent Expense for $4,000. This adjusting entry should have debited Rent Expense and credited Prepaid Rent for $4,000.

d. Debited Salary Expense and credited Accounts Payable to accrue salary expense of $12,000.

e. Recorded the earning of $7,800 service revenue collected in advance by debiting Accounts Receivable and crediting Service Revenue.

	Journal				
DATE (letter)	ACCOUNT TITLES AND EXPLANATIONS	POST REF.	DEBIT	CREDIT	

Journal

DATE (letter)		ACCOUNT TITLES AND EXPLANATIONS	POST REF.	DEBIT	CREDIT

*Exercise 4–15 (A1)

On December 31, 2017, Rexall Industries recorded an adjusting entry for $10,000 of accrued interest revenue. On January 15, 2018, the company received interest payments in the amount of $22,000. Assuming Rexall Industries uses reversing entries, prepare the 2017 and 2018 journal entries for these interest transactions.

Journal

DATE		ACCOUNT TITLES AND EXPLANATIONS	POST REF.	DEBIT	CREDIT

Exercise 4–17 ①

Refer to Exercise 3–22 of Chapter 3. Start from the unadjusted trial balance shown for Lee Management Consulting prepared at June 30, 2016:

Requirements 1–3

ACCOUNT TITLE	UNADJUSTED TRIAL BALANCE		ADJUSTMENTS	
	DEBIT	CREDIT	DEBIT	CREDIT
LEE MANAGEMENT CONSULTING				
Worksheet				
June 30, 2016				
Cash	23,750			
Accounts receivable	1,500			
Supplies	500			
Equipment	1,000			
Accum. amort.—equip.		0		
Furniture	5,000			
Accum. amort.—furn.		0		
Accounts payable		5,000		
Salaries payable		0		
Unearned revenue		2,000		
Michael Lee, capital		25,000		
Michael Lee, withdrawals	2,000			
Service revenue		5,000		
Rent expense	3,000			
Utilities expense	250			
Salaries expense	0			
Amort. expense—equip.	0			
Amort. expense—furn.	0			
Supplies expense	0			
	37,000	37,000		

At June 30, the company gathers the following information for the adjusting entries:

a. Accrued service revenue, $400.

b. Earned $800 of the service revenue collected in advance on June 21 for eight days of work.

c. Supplies remaining on hand at June 30, $100.

d. Amortization expense—equipment, $42; furniture, $167 (all amounts rounded to the nearest dollar).

e. Accrued $500 expense for the secretary's salary.

Required

1. Set up a worksheet using the unadjusted trial balance figures.

2. Enter the adjusting entries directly into the worksheet.

3. Complete all columns of the worksheet.

Requirements 1–3

LEE MANAGEMENT CONSULTING					
Worksheet					
June 30, 2016					
ADJUSTED TRIAL BALANCE		INCOME STATEMENT		BALANCE SHEET	
DEBIT	CREDIT	DEBIT	CREDIT	DEBIT	CREDIT

Exercise 4–18 ② ③ ⑤ ⑥

Start from the adjusted trial balance shown below that Lee Management Consulting prepared at June 30, 2016:

LEE MANAGEMENT CONSULTING		
Adjusted Trial Balance		
June 30, 2016		
Cash	$23,750	
Accounts receivable	1,900	
Supplies	100	
Equipment	1,000	
Accumulated amortization—equipment		$ 42
Furniture	5,000	
Accumulated amortization—furniture		167
Accounts payable		5,000
Salaries payable		500
Unearned revenue		1,200
Michael Lee, capital		25,000
Michael Lee, withdrawals	2,000	
Service revenue		6,200
Amortization expense—equipment	42	
Amortization expense—furniture	167	
Rent expense	3,000	
Salaries expense	500	
Supplies expense	400	
Utilities expense	250	
Total	$38,109	$38,109

Required

1. Journalize, with explanations, and post to T-accounts the closing entries at June 30, 2016. Denote each closing amount as *Clo.* and account balance as *Bal.*

2. Prepare a classified balance sheet in report format at June 30, 2016.

3. Compute the current ratio and the debt ratio of Lee Management Consulting and evaluate these ratio values as indicative of a strong or weak financial position.

4. Prepare a post-closing trial balance at June 30, 2016.

Requirement 1

	Journal				
DATE		ACCOUNT TITLES AND EXPLANATIONS	POST REF.	DEBIT	CREDIT

Requirement 1 (Continued)

Income Summary		Michael Lee, Capital	

Michael Lee, Withdrawals		Service Revenue	

Amortization Expense—Equipment		Amortization Expense—Furniture	

Rent Expense		Salaries Expense	

Supplies Expense		Utilities Expense	

Requirement 2

Requirement 3

Current ratio:

Debt ratio:

Requirement 4

LEE MANAGEMENT CONSULTING		
Post-Closing Trial Balance		
June 30, 2016		
ACCOUNT	DEBIT	CREDIT
Cash		
Accounts receivable		
Supplies		
Equipment		
Accumulated amortization—equipment		
Furniture		
Accumulated amortization-furniture		
Accounts payable		
Salaries payable		
Unearned revenue		
Michael Lee, capital		
Total		

Problem 4–1A ①

The unadjusted trial balance of Dorset Roofing at July 31, 2017, appears below:

ACCOUNT TITLE	UNDAJUSTED TRIAL BALANCE DEBIT	CREDIT	ADJUSTMENTS DEBIT	CREDIT
	DORSET ROOFING			
	Worksheet			
	July 31, 2017			
Cash	127,200			
Accounts receivable	226,920			
Supplies	105,960			
Prepaid insurance	23,800			
Equipment	196,140			
Accum. amort.—equip.		157,440		
Building	257,340			
Accum. amort.—building		63,000		
Land	179,800			
Accounts payable		136,140		
Interest payable		0		
Wages payable		0		
Unearned service revenue		63,360		
Notes payable, long-term		134,400		
T. Jackson, capital		474,780		
T. Jackson, withdrawals	25,200			
Service revenue		141,140		
Amort. expense—equip.	0			
Amort. expense—bldg.	0			
Wages expense	19,200			
Insurance expense	0			
Interest expense	0			
Utilities expense	6,660			
Advertising expense	2,040			
Supplies expense	0			
	1,170,260	1,170,260		

Additional data at July 31, 2017:

a. Amortization for the period to be recorded: equipment, $2,040; building, $4,210.

b. Wages expense to be recorded because employees worked but have not yet been paid, $3,440.

c. A count of supplies showed that unused supplies amounted to $88,440.

d. During July, $5,000 of prepaid insurance coverage was used.

e. Accrued interest expense, $2,080.

DORSET ROOFING					
Worksheet					
July 31, 2017					
ADJUSTED TRIAL BALANCE		INCOME STATEMENT		BALANCE SHEET	
DEBIT	CREDIT	DEBIT	CREDIT	DEBIT	CREDIT

f. Of the $63,360 balance of Unearned Service Revenue, $29,820 was earned during July.

g. Accrued advertising expense, $2,600 (credit Accounts Payable).

h. The company performed $9,600 of services for a client and has not yet been paid.

Required   Complete Dorset Roofing's worksheet for July. Identify each adjusting entry by its letter.

Problem 4–3A ① ② ③

The unadjusted trial balance of Byford Systems at December 31, 2017, and the related year-end adjustment data are given below.

Requirement 1

ACCOUNT TITLE	UNADJUSTED TRIAL BALANCE		ADJUSTMENTS	
	DEBIT	CREDIT	DEBIT	CREDIT
Cash	7,500			
Accounts receivable	54,000			
Supplies	13,500			
Equipment	148,500			
Accum. amort.—equip.		54,000		
Accounts payable		9,000		
Salary payable		0		
Unearned service revenue		7,500		
Note payable, long-term		90,000		
T. Byford, capital		54,000		
T. Byford, withdrawals	93,000			
Service revenue		223,500		
Salary expense	79,500			
Supplies expense	0			
Rent expense	22,500			
Amort. expense—equip.	0			
Interest expense	9,000			
Insurance expense	10,500			
	438,000	438,000		

Adjustment data at December 31, 2017, include the following:

a. Of the $7,500 balance of Unearned Service Revenue at the beginning of the year, all of it except $500 was earned during the year.
b. Supplies still unused at year end, $3,000.
c. Amortization for the year, $13,000.
d. Accrued salary expense, $4,000.
e. Accrued service revenue, $5,500.

Required

1. Write the account data in the Trial Balance columns of a worksheet and complete the worksheet. Identify each adjusting entry by the letter corresponding to the data given.
2. Journalize the adjusting and closing entries. Include explanations.

Requirement 1

ADJUSTED TRIAL BALANCE		INCOME STATEMENT		BALANCE SHEET	
DEBIT	CREDIT	DEBIT	CREDIT	DEBIT	CREDIT

Requirement 2

Journal

DATE		ACCOUNT TITLES AND EXPLANATIONS	POST REF.	DEBIT	CREDIT

Requirement 2 (Continued)

Journal				
DATE	ACCOUNT TITLES AND EXPLANATIONS	POST REF.	DEBIT	CREDIT

Problem 4–6A ② ③ ⑤ ⑥

The adjusted trial balance of Balti Design at June 30, 2017, the end of the company's fiscal year, appears below.

Required

1. Prepare the income statement and statement of owner's equity for the year ended June 30, 2017, and the classified balance sheet on that date. Use the account format for the balance sheet.
2. Journalize the closing entries.
3. Compute Balti Design's current ratio and debt ratio at June 30, 2017. One year ago the current ratio stood at 1.01 and the debt ratio was 0.71. Did Balti Design's ability to pay debts improve or deteriorate during the fiscal year?

BALTI DESIGN		
Adjusted Trial Balance		
June 30, 2017		
Cash	$ 12,610	
Accounts receivable	15,882	
Supplies	18,774	
Prepaid insurance	1,920	
Equipment	33,480	
Accumulated amortization—equipment		$ 9,888
Building	68,940	
Accumulated amortization—building		10,110
Land	18,000	
Accounts payable		25,040
Interest payable		1,894
Wages payable		1,462
Unearned service revenue		1,380
Notes payable, long-term		58,200
A. Kapoor, capital		41,034
A. Kapoor, withdrawals	28,180	
Service revenue		83,916
Amortization expense—equipment	4,380	
Amortization expense—building	2,382	
Wages expense	13,882	
Insurance expense	1,860	
Interest expense	7,906	
Utilities expense	2,580	
Supplies expense	2,148	
Total	$232,924	$232,924

Requirement 1

Requirement 1 (Continued)

Note: If needed, create a second dollar-column for assets.

Requirement 2

Journal				
DATE	ACCOUNT TITLES AND EXPLANATIONS	POST REF.	DEBIT	CREDIT

Requirement 3

Current ratio:

Debt ratio:

_____

_____

_____

_____

_____

_____

_____

Problem 4–7A ⑤ ⑥

The accounts of Bolton Travel at December 31, 2017, are listed below in alphabetical order:

Accounts Payable	$ 15,300	Interest Payable	$ 4,300
Accounts Receivable	19,800	Interest Receivable	1,600
Accumulated Amortization—Building	113,400	Land	62,500
Accumulated Amortization—Furniture	34,800	Notes Payable, Long-term	91,400
Advertising Expense	6,600	Notes Receivable, Long-term	12,500
Amortization Expense	3,900	Other Assets	9,300
Building	313,200	Other Current Liabilities	14,100
Cash	25,000	Prepaid Insurance	3,300
Commission Revenue	280,500	Prepaid Rent	12,700
E. Bolton, Capital	209,400	Salary Expense	73,800
E. Bolton, Withdrawals	143,800	Salary Payable	6,700
Furniture	68,100	Supplies	8,500
Insurance Expense	2,400	Supplies Expense	17,100
		Unearned Commission Revenue	14,200

Required

1. Prepare the company's classified balance sheet in report format at December 31, 2017. *All adjustments have been journalized and posted, but the closing entries have not yet been made.*

2. Compute Bolton Travel's current ratio and debt ratio at December 31, 2017. At December 31, 2016, the current ratio was 1.52 and the debt ratio was 0.37. Did Bolton Travel's ability to pay both current and total debts improve or deteriorate during 2017?

Requirement 1

Requirement 2

Current ratio:

Debt ratio:

5 MERCHANDISING OPERATIONS

LEARNING OBJECTIVES

1 Use sales and gross margin to evaluate a company.
2 Account for the purchase and sale of inventory under the perpetual inventory system.
3 Adjust and close the accounts of a merchandising business under the perpetual inventory system.
4 Prepare a merchandiser's financial statements under the perpetual inventory system.
5 Use the gross margin percentage and the inventory turnover ratio to evaluate a business.
6 Describe the merchandising operations effects of International Financial Reporting Standards (IFRS).

*A1 Account for the purchase and sale of inventory under the periodic system.
*A2 Compute the cost of goods sold under the periodic inventory system.
*A3 Adjust and close the accounts of a merchandising business under the periodic inventory system.
*A4 Prepare a merchandiser's financial statements under the periodic inventory system.
*B1 Compare the perpetual and periodic inventory systems.

Starter 5–6 ②

Details of purchase invoices, including shipping terms, credit terms, and returns, appear below. Compute the total amount to be paid in full settlement of each invoice, assuming that credit for returns is granted before the expiration of the discount period and payment is made within the discount period. (Hint: Assume FOB destination freight is included in the invoice price.)

Invoice	Freight and Credit Terms	Transportation Charges	Returns and Allowances
a. $2,000	FOB destination, 3/10, n/45	$ 55	$200
b. $5,500	FOB shipping point, 2/10, n/30	$100	$ 50
c. $6,700	FOB shipping point, 2/10, n/45	$200	$350
d. $9,300	FOB destination, 2/10, n/60	$150	$550

Starter 5–11 ③

Beachcombers Inc.'s Inventory account at year end showed a debit balance of $150,000. A physical count of inventory showed goods on hand of $147,000. Journalize the adjusting entry. Beachcombers uses the perpetual inventory system.

DATE	ACCOUNT TITLES AND EXPLANATIONS	POST REF.	DEBIT	CREDIT

Journal

*Starter 5–17 ⑤ Ⓐ① Ⓐ② Ⓑ①

For each statement below, identify whether the statement applies to the periodic inventory system or the perpetual inventory system:

a. Normally used for relatively inexpensive goods.

b. Keeps a running computerized record of merchandise inventory.

c. Achieves better control over merchandise inventory.

d. Requires a physical count of inventory to determine the quantities on hand.

e. Uses bar codes to keep up-to-the-minute records of inventory.

a. _____

b. _____

c. _____

d. _____

e. _____

Starter 5–18 ⑥

What are two key criteria that merchandisers who report under IFRS must follow? Do these criteria differ from those followed by companies that report under ASPE?

_____

_____

_____

_____

_____

_____

_____

_____

_____

_____

_____

_____

Exercise 5–2 ①

Supply the missing income statement amounts in each of the following situations:

Sales	Sales Discounts	Net Sales	Cost of Goods Sold	Gross Margin
$94,500	$2,200	$92,300	$56,700	(a) _____
99,500	(b) _____	95,520	(c) _____	$36,000
68,700	2,100	(d) _____	37,700	(e) _____
(f) _____	3,500	(g) _____	52,500	18,600

Calculations

_____

_____

_____

_____

_____

_____

_____

_____

_____

_____

Exercise 5–3 ②

Suppose Sears uses the perpetual inventory system and purchases $300,000 of sporting goods on account from Nike on April 10, 2017. Credit terms are 1/10, net 30. Sears pays electronically, and Nike receives the money on April 20, 2017.

Journalize Sears' (a) purchase and (b) cash payment transactions. What was Sears' net cost of this inventory?

Note: Exercise 5–4 covers this same situation for the seller.

	Journal			
DATE	ACCOUNT TITLES AND EXPLANATIONS	POST REF.	DEBIT	CREDIT

Exercise 5–4 ②

Nike uses the perpetual inventory system and sells $300,000 of sporting goods to Sears under credit terms of 1/10, net 30 on April 10, 2017. Nike's cost of the goods is $210,000, and it receives the appropriate amount of cash from Sears on April 20, 2017.

Journalize Nike's transactions on April 10, 2017, and April 20, 2017. How much gross margin did Nike earn on this sale?

	Journal			
DATE	ACCOUNT TITLES AND EXPLANATIONS	POST REF.	DEBIT	CREDIT

Exercise 5–9 ① ③

Bubble Tea's accounts at December 31, 2017, included these unadjusted balances:

Inventory..	$ 4,400
Cost of Goods Sold......................................	31,200
Sales Revenue...	46,800
Sales Discounts...	1,250
Sales Returns and Allowances..................	700

The physical count of inventory showed $3,700 of inventory on hand. This is the only adjustment needed.

Required

1. Journalize the adjustment for inventory shrinkage. Include an explanation. Bubble Tea uses the perpetual inventory system.
2. Journalize the closing entries for the appropriate accounts.
3. Compute the gross margin.

Requirements 1 & 2

Journal

DATE	ACCOUNT TITLES AND EXPLANATIONS	POST REF.	DEBIT	CREDIT

Requirement 3 — Gross Margin

_____

_____

_____

_____

_____

_____

_____

Exercise 5–10 ③

The Trial Balance and Adjustments columns of the worksheet of Wells Decorating Centre included these accounts and balances at December 31, 2017:

Account Title	Trial Balance Debit	Trial Balance Credit	Adjustments Debit	Adjustments Credit
Cash	17,000			
Accounts receivable	27,500		(a) 2,200	
Inventory	63,500			(b) 1,400
Supplies	18,600			(c) 6,400
Store fixtures	70,000			
Accumulated amortization		35,000		(d) 7,000
Accounts payable		31,200		
Salary payable		0		(e) 3,800
Note payable, long-term		12,500		
B. Wells, capital		41,800		
B. Wells, withdrawals	34,000			
Sales revenue		431,400		(a) 2,200
Sales discounts	4,300			
Cost of goods sold	244,400		(b) 1,400	
Selling expenses	42,800		(c) 5,200	
			(e) 3,800	
General expenses	28,700		(c) 1,200	
			(d) 7,000	
Interest expense	1,100			
Total	551,900	551,900	20,800	20,800

Required

Wells Decorating Centre uses the perpetual inventory system. Compute the adjusted balance for each account that must be closed. Then journalize Wells Decorating Centre's closing entries at December 31, 2017. How much was Wells Decorating Centre's net income or net loss?

Journal

DATE	ACCOUNT TITLES AND EXPLANATIONS	POST REF.	DEBIT	CREDIT

Net Income = _____

Exercise 5–11 ④

Use the data in Exercise 5–10 to prepare the multi-step income statement of Wells Decorating Centre for the year ended December 31, 2017.

Exercise 5–15 ⑤

Networking Systems, which uses the perpetual inventory system, earned sales revenue of $66 million in 2017. Cost of goods sold was $35 million, and net income reached $16 million, Networking's highest ever. Total current assets included inventory of $14.0 million at December 31, 2017. Last year's ending inventory was $13.2 million. The managers of Networking Systems need to know the company's gross margin percentage and rate of inventory turnover for 2017. Compute these amounts.

Gross margin   =
   percentage

Inventory   =
   turnover

Extra Journal Page

DATE		ACCOUNTS TITLES AND EXPLANATIONS	POST REF.	DEBIT	CREDIT

*Exercise 5–16 Ⓐ1

Journalize, without explanations, the following transactions of Digbey Auto Parts, a distributor that uses the periodic inventory system, during the month of June 2017:

Jun. 3 Purchased $16,800 of inventory under terms of 2/10, n/eom and FOB shipping point.

7 Returned $1,600 of defective merchandise purchased on June 3.

9 Paid freight bill of $350 on June 3 purchase.

10 Sold inventory for $22,400, collecting cash of $3,600. Payment terms on the remainder were 2/15, n/30.

12 Paid amount owed on credit purchase of June 3.

16 Granted a sales allowance of $1,200 on the June 10 sale.

23 Received cash from the June 10 customer in full settlement of the debt.

	Journal				
DATE		ACCOUNT TITLES AND EXPLANATIONS	POST REF.	DEBIT	CREDIT

*Exercise 5–25 ① Ⓐ2

Rees Distributors uses the periodic inventory system. Rees reported these amounts at May 31, 2017:

Inventory, May 31, 2016...	$29,000
Inventory, May 31, 2017...	31,000
Purchases (of inventory)..	82,000
Purchase Discounts..	2,000
Purchase Returns...	3,000
Freight-in..	4,000
Sales Revenue..	200,000
Sales Discounts...	13,000
Sales Returns..	15,000

Compute Rees Distributors':

a. Net sales revenue

b. Cost of goods sold

c. Gross margin

a. – c.

Exercise 5–27 ② ③ ④ ⑤

Lee Management Consulting performs services but also began selling software. Lee Management uses the perpetual inventory system. During July 2016, the business completed these transactions:

July   2   Completed a consulting engagement and received cash of $7,200.

       2   Prepaid three months' office rent, $9,000.

       7   Purchased 100 units of software inventory on account, $1,900, plus owed the manufacturer freight-in of $100.

     16   Paid employee salary, $2,000. (Note previous year-end accrual of $500.)

     18   Sold 70 software units on account, $3,100 (cost $1,400).

     19   Consulted with a client for a fee of $900 on account.

     21   Paid on account, $2,000.

     22   Purchased 200 units of software inventory on account, $4,600.

     24   Paid utilities, $300.

     28   Sold 100 units of software for cash, $4,000 (cost $2,210).

     31   Recorded the following adjusting entries:
           Accrued salary expense, $1,000.
           Prepaid rent used, $3,000.
           Amortization of office furniture, $167, and of equipment, $42.
           Physical count of inventory, 120 units, $2,760.

Required

1. Open the following selected T-accounts in the ledger with their normal opening balances as shown: Cash, $23,750; Accounts Receivable, $1,900; Software Inventory, $0; Prepaid Rent, $0; Supplies, $100; Equipment, $1,000; Accumulated Amortization—Equipment, $42; Furniture, $5,000; Accumulated Amortization—Furniture, $167; Accounts Payable, $5,000; Salaries Payable, $500; Unearned Revenue, $1,200; Michael Lee, Capital, $24,841; Income Summary, $0; Service Revenue, $0; Sales Revenue, $0; Cost of Goods Sold, $0; Salaries Expense, $0; Rent Expense, $0; Utilities Expense, $0; Amortization Expense—Equipment, $0; and Amortization Expense—Furniture, $0.

2. Journalize and post to the T-accounts the July transactions. Reference all transactions by date. Total each T-account, where applicable, and denote the balance as *Bal.*

3. Journalize and post the closing entries. Denote each closing amount as *Clo.*

4. Prepare the July 2016 income statement of Lee Management Consulting. Use the single-step format. (*Hint:* List each type of revenue separately in the Revenues section of the income statement.)

Requirements 1, 2, & 3

Cash	Accounts Receivable	Software Inventory

Prepaid Rent	Supplies	Equipment

Requirements 1, 2, & 3 (Continued)

| Accumulated Amortization—Equipment | Furniture | Accumulated Amortization—Furniture |

| Accounts Payable | Salaries Payable | Unearned Revenue |

| M. Lee, Capital | Service Revenue | Sales Revenue |

| Cost of Goods Sold | Salaries Expense | Rent Expense |

| Utilities Expense | Amortization Expense—Equipment | Amortization Expense—Furniture |

Income Summary

Requirements 2 & 3

		Journal			
DATE		ACCOUNT TITLES AND EXPLANATIONS	POST REF.	DEBIT	CREDIT

Requirements 2 & 3 (Continued)

Journal				
DATE	ACCOUNT TITLES AND EXPLANATIONS	POST REF.	DEBIT	CREDIT

Requirement 4

Problem 5–3A ②

Singh Distributing Company uses the perpetual inventory system and engaged in the following transactions during May of the current year:

May	3	Purchased office supplies for cash, $22,000.
	7	Purchased inventory on credit terms of 3/10, net eom, $76,000.
	8	Returned 25 percent of the inventory purchased on May 7. It was not the inventory ordered.
	10	Sold goods for cash, $34,000 (cost, $20,400).
	13	Sold inventory on credit terms of 2/15, n/45 for $150,800, less $15,080 quantity discount offered to customers who purchase in large quantities (cost, $90,480).
	16	Paid the amount owed on account from the purchase of May 7, less the discount and the return.
	17	Received wrong-sized inventory as a sales return from May 13 sale, $12,400, which is the net amount after the quantity discount. Singh's cost of the inventory received was $7,440.
	18	Purchased inventory of $164,000 on account. Payment terms were 2/10, net 30.
	26	Paid supplier for goods purchased on May 18.
	28	Received cash in full settlement of the account from the customer who purchased inventory on May 13.
	31	Purchased inventory for cash, $96,000, less a quantity discount of $9,600, plus freight charges of $2,200.

Required

1. Journalize the preceding transactions on the books of Singh Distributing Company.
2. Suppose the balance in Inventory was $20,000 on May 1. What is the balance in inventory on May 31?

Requirement 1

	Journal			
DATE	ACCOUNT TITLES AND EXPLANATIONS	POST REF.	DEBIT	CREDIT

Requirement 1 (Continued)

Journal

DATE	ACCOUNT TITLES AND EXPLANATIONS	POST REF.	DEBIT	CREDIT

Requirement 2

Inventory

Problem 5–6A ④

Items from the accounts of Marchand Distributors at May 31, 2017, follow, listed in alphabetical order. Marchand Distributors uses the perpetual inventory system. For simplicity, the operating expenses are summarized in the General Expenses and the Selling Expenses accounts.

Accounts Payable	$ 51,000	Interest Payable	$ 2,800
Accounts Receivable	107,500	Interest Revenue	600
Accumulated Amortization—Equipment	96,900	Inventory, May 31, 2017	147,100
C. Marchand, Capital	167,800	Notes Payable, Long-Term	114,800
C. Marchand, Withdrawals	66,900	Salaries Payable	7,200
Cash	19,900	Sales Discounts	26,500
Cost of Goods Sold	1,086,900	Sales Returns and Allowances	45,900
Equipment	340,800	Sales Revenue	1,991,500
General Expenses	206,800	Selling Expenses	357,200
Interest Expense	9,200	Supplies	33,100
		Unearned Sales Revenue	15,200

Required

1. Prepare the business's single-step income statement for the year ended May 31, 2017.
2. Prepare the statement of owner's equity for the year ended May 31, 2017.
3. Prepare Marchand Distributors' classified balance sheet in report format at May 31, 2017.

Requirement 1

Requirement 2

Requirement 3

Problem 5-7A ④⑤

1. Use the data in Problem 5-6A to prepare Marchand Distributors' multi-step income statement for the year ended May 31, 2017.

2. Corry Marchand, owner of the company, strives to earn a gross margin of at least 50 percent and a net income of 20 percent (Net income percentage = Net income ÷ Net sales revenue). Did Marchand Distributors achieve these goals? Show your calculations.

Requirement 1

Requirement 2

Gross margin   =
    percentage

Net income   =
    percentage

Problem 5–9A ③④⑤

Buono Adventures, which uses the perpetual inventory system, has the following account balances (in alphabetical order) on July 31, 2017:

Accounts Payable..	$ 21,600
Accounts Receivable...	23,200
Accumulated Amortization—Equipment...............	64,600
Cash..	8,400
Cost of Goods Sold..	687,000
E. Buono, Capital...	402,000
E. Buono, Withdrawals...	92,000
Equipment...	180,000
Interest Earned...	4,000
Inventory...	143,000
Operating Expenses...	355,000
Sales Discounts..	10,300
Sales Returns and Allowances......................................	32,900
Sales Revenue...	1,045,200
Supplies..	14,600
Unearned Sales Revenue..	9,000

Note: For simplicity, all operating expenses have been summarized in the account Operating Expenses.

Additional data at July 31, 2017:

a. A physical count of items showed $3,000 of supplies on hand. (*Hint:* Use the account Operating Expenses in the adjusting journal entry.)

b. An inventory count showed inventory on hand at July 31, 2017, of $140,000.

c. The equipment has an estimated useful life of eight years and is expected to have no value at the end of its life. (*Hint:* Use the account Operating Expenses in the adjusting journal entry.)

d. Unearned sales revenue of $5,600 was earned by July 31, 2017.

Required

1. Record all adjustments and closing entries that would be required on July 31, 2017.
2. Prepare the financial statements of Buono Adventures for the year ended July 31, 2017.

Requirement 1

Journal

DATE		ACCOUNT TITLES AND EXPLANATIONS	POST REF.	DEBIT	CREDIT

Requirement 2

Requirement 2 (Continued)

*Problem 5–12A Ⓐ③

The trial balance of Marvin's Fine Gems at December 31, 2017, is shown below:

MARVIN'S FINE GEMS		
Trial Balance		
December 31, 2017		
Cash	$ 6,200	
Accounts receivable	57,000	
Inventory	345,000	
Prepaid rent	28,000	
Equipment	108,000	
Accumulated amortization—equipment		$ 43,200
Accounts payable		43,200
Salary payable		0
Interest payable		0
Note payable, long-term		87,000
J. Marvin, capital		270,000
J. Marvin, withdrawals	153,000	
Sales revenue		835,400
Purchases	337,800	
Salary expense	118,600	
Rent expense	44,000	
Advertising expense	21,600	
Utilities expense	30,800	
Amortization expense—equipment	0	
Insurance expense	13,200	
Interest expense	2,600	
Miscellaneous expense	13,000	
Total	$1,278,800	$1,278,800

Additional data at December 31, 2017:

a. Rent expense for the year, $48,000.

b. The equipment has an estimated useful life of 10 years and is expected to have no value when it is retired from service.

c. Accrued salaries at December 31, $7,000.

d. Accrued interest expense at December 31, $2,600.

e. Inventory based on the inventory count on December 31, 2017, $351,200.

Required Complete Marvin's Fine Gems' worksheet for the year ended December 31, 2017. Marvin's Fine Gems uses the periodic inventory system.

MARVIN'S FINE GEMS
Worksheet
For the Year Ended December 31, 2017

ACCOUNT TITLE	UNADJUSTED TRIAL BALANCE		ADJUSTMENTS		INCOME STATEMENT		BALANCE SHEET	
	DEBIT	CREDIT	DEBIT	CREDIT	DEBIT	CREDIT	DEBIT	CREDIT
Cash	$ 6,200							
Accounts receivable	57,000							
Inventory	345,000							
Prepaid rent	28,000							
Equipment	108,000							
Accum. amort.—equipment		$ 43,200						
Accounts payable		43,200						
Salary payable		0						
Interest payable		0						
Note payable, long-term		87,000						
J. Marvin, capital		270,000						
J. Marvin, withdrawals	153,000							
Sales revenue		835,400						
Purchases	337,800							
Salary expense	118,600							
Rent expense	44,000							
Advertising expense	21,600							
Utilities expense	30,800							
Amortization exp.—equipment	0							
Insurance expense	13,200							
Interest expense	2,600							
Miscellaneous expense	13,000							
	$1,278,800	$1,278,800						
Net income								

*Problem 5–13A Ⓐ⑶

Refer to the data in Problem 5–12A.

Required

1. Journalize the adjusting and closing entries.
2. Determine the December 31, 2017, balance of Capital for Marvin's Fine Gems.

Requirement 1

Journal

DATE	ACCOUNT TITLES AND EXPLANATIONS	POST REF.	DEBIT	CREDIT

Requirement 2 (December 31, 2017, balance of capital)

J. Marvin, Capital

*Problem 5–14A Ⓐ

Items from the accounts of Marchand Distributors at May 31, 2017, follow, listed in alphabetical order. Marchand Distributors uses the periodic inventory system. For simplicity, all operating expenses are summarized in the General Expenses and the Selling Expenses account.

Accounts Payable	$ 71,000	Inventory May 31, 2016	$ 151,800
Accounts Receivable	107,500	Notes Payable, Long-Term	114,800
Accumulated Amortization—Equipment	96,900	Purchases	1,102,200
C. Marchand, Capital	167,800	Salaries Payable	7,200
C. Marchand, Withdrawals	66,900	Sales Discounts	26,500
Cash	19,900	Sales Returns and Allowances	45,900
Equipment	340,800	Sales Revenue	1,991,500
General Expenses	206,800	Selling Expenses	357,200
Interest Expense	9,200	Supplies	33,100
Interest Payable	2,800	Unearned Sales Revenue	15,200
Interest Revenue	600		

Required

1. Prepare the business's single-step income statement for the year ended May 31, 2017. A physical count of inventory on May 31, 2017, valued it at $167,100.
2. Prepare Marchand Distributors' statement of owner's equity at May 31, 2017.
3. Prepare Marchand Distributors' classified balance sheet in report format at May 31, 2017.

Requirement 1

Requirement 2

Requirement 3

	Extra Journal Page			
DATE	ACCOUNTS TITLES AND EXPLANATIONS	POST REF.	DEBIT	CREDIT

6 ACCOUNTING FOR MERCHANDISE INVENTORY

LEARNING OBJECTIVES

1 Account for perpetual inventory under the specific-unit-cost, FIFO, and moving-weighted-average-cost methods.
2 Compare the effects of the FIFO and moving-weighted-average-cost methods.
3 Account for periodic inventory under the FIFO and weighted-average-cost methods.
4 Apply the lower-of-cost-and-net-realizable-value rule to inventory.
5 Measure the effects of inventory errors.
6 Estimate ending inventory by the gross margin method and the retail method.

Starter 6–1 ①

Terget Company has the following items in its inventory on August 1:

Serial Number	Cost
661	$ 9,100
665	9,300
668	8,700
675	10,950

The company uses the specific-unit-cost method for costing inventory. During August, it sold units 661 and 668 for $15,000 each and purchased unit 676 for $11,200. What is the value of the ending inventory at August 31?

_____

_____

_____

_____

_____

Starter 6–9 ③

Kim's Dry Goods uses a periodic inventory system. Kim's completed the following inventory transactions during April, its first month of operations:

Apr.	1	Purchased 10 shirts at $50 each
	7	Sold 6 shirts for $80 each
	13	Purchased 6 shirts for $55 each
	21	Sold 3 shirts for $85 each

Compute Kim's ending inventory and cost of goods sold under FIFO costing. Then compute ending inventory and cost of goods sold under the weighted-average-cost method. Round average unit cost to the nearest cent. Compute gross margin under both methods. Which method results in the higher gross margin?

	FIFO	Weighted Average

Starter 6–10 ④

On the basis of the following data, determine the value of the inventory at the lower of cost and net realizable value:

Item	Quantity	Cost Price/Unit	Market Price/Unit	Selling Costs
001	5	$29	$30	$100
002	8	$40	$35	$ 50

Starter 6–11 (5)

Clinton Cycles uses a periodic inventory system. The inventory data for the year ended December 31, 2016, follow:

Sales revenue	$150,000
Cost of goods sold:	
Beginning inventory	22,000
Net purchases	80,000
Cost of goods available for sale	102,000
Less: Ending inventory	(24,000)
Cost of goods sold	78,000
Gross margin	$72,000

Assume that the ending inventory was accidentally overstated by $4,000. What are the correct amounts of cost of goods sold and gross margin after correcting this error?

_____

_____

_____

_____

_____

_____

_____

_____

Starter 6–13 (6)

Wesley Carpets began the year with inventory of $1,400,000. Inventory purchases for the year totalled $3,200,000. Sales revenue for the year was $7,000,000 and the gross margin was 40 percent. How much is Wesley Carpets's estimated cost of ending inventory? Use the gross margin method.

Exercise 6–2 ①

Creative Kaos Store carries a large inventory of guitars and other musical instruments. The store uses the FIFO method and a perpetual inventory system. Company records indicate the following for a particular line of guitars:

Date		Item	Quantity	Unit Cost
May	1	Balance	5	$900
	6	Sale	3	
	8	Purchase	10	840
	17	Sale	4	
	30	Purchase	5	840

Required Prepare a perpetual inventory record for the guitars. Then determine the amounts Creative Kaos Store should report for ending inventory and cost of goods sold under the FIFO method.

Perpetual Inventory Record

ITEM:

		PURCHASES			COST OF GOODS SOLD			INVENTORY ON HAND	
DATE	QTY.	UNIT COST	TOTAL COST	QTY.	UNIT COST	TOTAL COST	QTY.	UNIT COST	TOTAL COST

Calculations:

Exercise 6–3 ①

After preparing the FIFO perpetual inventory record in Exercise 6–2, journalize Creative Kaos Store's May 8 purchase of inventory on account and the cash sale on May 17 (sale price of each guitar was $1,600).

DATE		ACCOUNT TITLES AND EXPLANATIONS	POST REF.	DEBIT	CREDIT

Table title: Journal

Exercise 6–4 ①

Refer to the Creative Kaos Store inventory data in Exercise 6–2, except assume that the store uses the moving-weighted-average-cost method. Prepare Creative Kaos Store's perpetual inventory record for the guitars on the moving-weighted-average-cost basis. Round average cost per unit to the nearest cent and all other amounts to the nearest dollar.

Perpetual Inventory Record

ITEM:

		PURCHASES			COST OF GOODS SOLD			INVENTORY ON HAND		
DATE	QTY.	UNIT COST	TOTAL COST	QTY.	UNIT COST	TOTAL COST	QTY.	UNIT COST	TOTAL COST

Calculations:

Exercise 6–5 ②

Use your results from Exercises 6–2 and 6–4 to calculate the gross margin for Creative Kaos Store under both the FIFO and the moving-weighted-average-cost methods. Explain why the gross margin is higher under the moving-weighted-average-cost method.

	FIFO	Moving-Weighted-Average

_____

_____

_____

_____

Exercise 6–9 ③

Kelso Electrical's inventory records for industrial switches indicate the following at November 30, 2017:

Nov.	1	Beginning inventory	14 units at $160
	8	Purchase	4 units at $170
	15	Purchase	11 units at $180
	26	Purchase	5 units at $190

The physical count of inventory at November 30, 2017, indicates that six units remain in ending inventory and the company owns them.

Required   Compute ending inventory and cost of goods sold using each of the following methods, assuming a periodic inventory system is used:

1. Specific-unit cost, assuming three $170 units and three $180 units are on hand on November 30, 2017
2. Weighted-average cost
3. First-in, first-out (FIFO) cost

Requirements 1 – 3

	ENDING INVENTORY	COST OF GOODS SOLD
1. SPECIFIC-UNIT COST:		

2. WEIGHTED-AVERAGE COST:

3. FIFO COST:

Exercise 6–13 ③ ④

Wire Solutions Company's income statement for the month ended August 31, 2017, reported the following data:

Income Statement

Sales revenue		$320,000
Cost of goods sold:		
Beginning inventory	$ 82,000	
Net purchases	243,700	
Cost of goods available for sale	325,700	
Ending inventory	105,700	
Cost of goods sold		220,000
Gross margin		$100,000

Before the financial statements were released, it was discovered that the current net realizable value of ending inventory was $96,000.

1. Journalize the entry to apply the lower-of-cost-and-net-realizable-value rule to the inventory.

2. Prepare a revised income statement to adjust the preceding income statement to apply the lower-of-cost-and-net-realizable-value rule to Wire Solutions Company's inventory. Also show the relevant portion of Wire Solutions Company's balance sheet.

Requirement 1

Journal				
DATE	ACCOUNT TITLES AND EXPLANATIONS	POST REF.	DEBIT	CREDIT

Requirement 2

Exercise 6–20 ②

Consider the following July 2016 transactions for Lee Management Consulting, which were also presented in Chapter 5:

Jul.	2	Completed a consulting engagement and received cash of $7,200.
	2	Prepaid three months' office rent, $9,000.
	7	Purchased 100 units of software inventory on account, $1,900, plus owed the manufacturer freight-in of $100.
	16	Paid employee salary, $2,000. (Note previous year-end accrual of $500.)
	18	Sold 70 software units on account, $3,100 (cost $1,400)
	19	Consulted with a client for a fee of $900 on account.
	21	Paid $2,000 on account for the July 7 purchase.
	22	Purchased 200 units of software inventory on account, $4,600.
	24	Paid utilities, $300 cash.
	28	Sold 100 units of software for cash, $4,000.
	31	Recorded the following adjusting entries:

        Accrued salary expense, $1,000.

        Prepaid rent used, $3,000.

        Amortization of office furniture, $167, and of equipment, $42.

        Physical count of inventory, 120 units, $2,713.

Required

1. Prepare perpetual inventory records for July for Lee Management Consulting using the moving-weighted-average perpetual method. Round average cost per unit to the nearest cent and all other amounts to the nearest dollar. (*Note:* You must calculate cost of goods sold for the July 18, 22, 28, and 31 transactions.)

2. Journalize and post to T-accounts the July transactions using the perpetual inventory record created in Requirement 1. Key all items by date. *Use the opening balances given in Serial Exercise 5–27 on page 301 of the textbook (also provided on the following pages).* Compute each account balance, and denote the balance as *Bal.* (*Adjusting entries are recorded in Requirement 3.*)

3. Journalize and post to T-accounts the adjusting entries. Denote each adjusting amount as *Adj.* After posting all adjusting entries, prove that the debits equal the credits by completing a trial balance.

Requirement 1

Perpetual Inventory Record

ITEM:

		PURCHASES			COST OF GOODS SOLD			INVENTORY ON HAND	
DATE	QTY.	UNIT COST	TOTAL COST	QTY.	UNIT COST	TOTAL COST	QTY.	UNIT COST	TOTAL COST

Requirement 2

	Journal			
DATE	ACCOUNT TITLES AND EXPLANATIONS	POST REF.	DEBIT	CREDIT

Requirements 2 & 3

Cash				Accounts Receivable	
Bal.	23,750		Bal.	1,900	

Inventory				Supplies	
Bal.	0		Bal.	100	

Prepaid Rent				Equipment	
			Bal.	1,000	

Accumulated Amortization—Equipment				Furniture	
	Bal.	42	Bal.	5,000	

Requirements 2 & 3 (Continued)

Accumulated Amortization—Furniture	
	Bal. 167

Accounts Payable	
	Bal. 5,000

Salaries Payable	
	Bal. 500

Unearned Revenue	
	Bal. 1,200

Michael Lee, Capital	
	Bal. 24,841

Michael Lee, Withdrawals	
Bal. 0	

Service Revenue

Sales Revenue

Requirements 2 & 3 (Continued)

Cost of Goods Sold

Amortization Expense—Equipment

Amortization Expense—Furniture

Rent Expense

Salaries Expense

Utilities Expense

Requirement 3

		Journal			
DATE		ACCOUNT TITLES AND EXPLANATIONS	POST REF.	DEBIT	CREDIT

Requirement 3 (Continued)

Problem 6–2A ①

Vista Distributors purchases inventory in crates of merchandise. Assume the company began July with an inventory of 30 units that cost $300 each. During the month, the company purchased and sold merchandise on account as shown:

Jul.	10	Purchased 30 units at $320
	15	Sold 40 units at $700
	22	Purchased 70 units at $350
	29	Sold 75 units at $800

Assume Vista Distributors uses the FIFO cost method for valuing inventories. The company uses a perpetual inventory system. Cash payments on account totalled $15,000. Company operating expenses for the month were $30,000. The company paid one-half in cash, with the rest accrued as Accounts Payable.

Required

1. Prepare a perpetual inventory record, at FIFO cost, for this merchandise.
2. Make journal entries to record the company's transactions.

Requirement 1

Perpetual Inventory Record

ITEM:

| | | PURCHASES | | | COST OF GOODS SOLD | | | INVENTORY ON HAND | |
| | | UNIT | TOTAL | | UNIT | TOTAL | | UNIT | TOTAL |
DATE	QTY.	COST	COST	QTY.	COST	COST	QTY.	COST	COST

Requirement 2

		Journal			
DATE		ACCOUNT TITLES AND EXPLANATIONS	POST REF.	DEBIT	CREDIT

Problem 6–3A ①

Refer to the Vista Distributors situation in Problem 6–2A. Keep all the data unchanged, except assume that Vista uses the moving-weighted-average-cost method.

Required

1. Prepare a perpetual inventory record at moving-weighted-average cost. Round the average unit cost to the nearest cent and all other amounts to the nearest dollar.

2. Prepare a multi-step income statement for Vista Distributors for the month of January.

Requirement 1

Perpetual Inventory Record

ITEM:

DATE	QTY.	PURCHASES UNIT COST	PURCHASES TOTAL COST	QTY.	COST OF GOODS SOLD UNIT COST	COST OF GOODS SOLD TOTAL COST	QTY.	INVENTORY ON HAND UNIT COST	INVENTORY ON HAND TOTAL COST

Requirement 2

Problem 6–5A ① ②

Sandy's Office Supplies distributes office furniture. The company's fiscal year ends on March 31, 2017. On January 31, 2017, one department in the company had in inventory 20 office suites that cost $1,800 each. During the quarter, the department purchased merchandise on account as follows:

	Units	Unit Cost	Total
January	60	$1,850	$111,000
February	40	1,900	76,000
March	30	1,950	58,500

Sales for each month in the quarter were as follows:

	Units	Unit Selling Price	Total
January	50	$3,600	$180,000
February	20	3,700	74,000
March	34	3,800	129,200

Operating expenses in the quarter were $110,000.

Assume that the company uses a perpetual inventory system. Also assume that monthly purchases of inventory occur on the first day of each month.

Required

1. Determine the cost of the department's ending inventory at March 31, 2017, under (a) moving-weighted-average costing and (b) FIFO costing.

2. Prepare the department's income statement for the quarter ended March 31, 2017, under each method described in Requirement 1. Show gross margin and operating income and note the difference.

Requirement 1

a.

Perpetual Inventory Record										
ITEM:										
		PURCHASES			COST OF GOODS SOLD			INVENTORY ON HAND		
DATE	QTY.	UNIT COST	TOTAL COST	QTY.	UNIT COST	TOTAL COST	QTY.	UNIT COST	TOTAL COST	

b.

Perpetual Inventory Record

ITEM:

DATE	QTY.	PURCHASES UNIT COST	PURCHASES TOTAL COST	QTY.	COST OF GOODS SOLD UNIT COST	COST OF GOODS SOLD TOTAL COST	QTY.	INVENTORY ON HAND UNIT COST	INVENTORY ON HAND TOTAL COST

Requirement 2

	MOVING-WEIGHTED-AVERAGE	FIFO

Problem 6–8A ③

Fast Framing Co. began March with 73 units of inventory that cost $50 each. During the month, Fast made the following purchases:

Mar.	4	113 units at $48
	12	81 units at $49
	19	167 units at $52
	25	34 units at $56

The company uses a periodic inventory system, and the physical count at March 31 shows 51 units of inventory on hand.

Required

1. Determine the ending inventory and cost of goods sold amounts for the March financial statements under (a) weighted-average cost and (b) FIFO cost. Round average cost per unit to the nearest cent and all other amounts to the nearest dollar.

2. Sales revenue for March totalled $40,000. Compute Fast's gross margin for March under each method.

3. Which method will result in lower income taxes for Fast? Why?

4. Which method will result in higher net income for Fast? Why?

Requirement 1

(a) WEIGHTED-AVERAGE COST

(b) FIFO COST

Requirement 2

	WEIGHTED-AVERAGE	FIFO

Requirement 3

Requirement 4

Problem 6–15A ① ⑤ ⑥

Toffler Auto Parts uses a perpetual inventory system for the purchase and sale of inventory and had the following information available on November 30, 2017:

		Purchases and Sales	Number of Units	Cost or Selling Price per Unit
Nov.	1	Balance of inventory	3,900	$40
	7	Purchased	6,000	56
	8	Sold	4,500	76
	12	Purchased	7,500	52
	16	Sold	9,000	84
	21	Purchased	4,500	52
	25	Purchased	10,500	48
	29	Sold	13,500	84

Required

1. Calculate the cost of goods sold and the cost of the ending inventory for November under each of the following inventory costing methods: (a) moving-weighted-average cost and (b) FIFO cost.

2. Prepare the journal entries required to record the transactions using the perpetual inventory system with FIFO costing.

3. An internal audit has discovered that a new employee—an accounting clerk—had been stealing merchandise and covering up the shortage by changing the inventory records.

    The external auditors examined the accounting records prior to the employment of the individual and noted that the company has an average gross margin rate of 35 percent. Use the gross margin method to estimate the cost of the inventory shortage (under the FIFO costing method). (*Note:* The physical count matched the estimate.) Explain the difference between the three inventory values—the accounting records, physical count, and estimates—and their importance in valuing inventory.

4. What would be the effect on the financial statements for the year ending November 30, 2017, if the inventory shortage had not been discovered?

Requirement 1

Perpetual Inventory Record

ITEM:

DATE	QTY.	PURCHASES UNIT COST	PURCHASES TOTAL COST	QTY.	COST OF GOODS SOLD UNIT COST	COST OF GOODS SOLD TOTAL COST	QTY.	INVENTORY ON HAND UNIT COST	INVENTORY ON HAND TOTAL COST

Perpetual Inventory Record

ITEM:

DATE	QTY.	PURCHASES UNIT COST	PURCHASES TOTAL COST	QTY.	COST OF GOODS SOLD UNIT COST	COST OF GOODS SOLD TOTAL COST	QTY.	INVENTORY ON HAND UNIT COST	INVENTORY ON HAND TOTAL COST

Requirement 2

Journal

DATE	ACCOUNT TITLES AND EXPLANATIONS	POST REF.	DEBIT	CREDIT

Requirements 3 & 4

Extra Journal Paper

DATE		ACCOUNTS TITLES AND EXPLANATIONS	POST REF.	DEBIT	CREDIT

7 ACCOUNTING INFORMATION SYSTEMS

LEARNING OBJECTIVES

1 Describe an effective accounting system.
2 Understand the elements of computerized and manual accounting systems.
3 Journalize and post transactions using the sales journal, the cash receipts journal, and the accounts receivable subsidiary ledger.
4 Journalize and post transactions using the purchases journal, the cash payments journal, and the accounts payable subsidiary ledger.
5 Journalize and post entries not recorded in a special journal.

*A1 Use special journals to record and post transactions with sales taxes.

Starter 7–4 ① ②

Complete the crossword puzzle.

Across:

2. Electronic linkage that allows different computers to share the same information
3. Main computer in a networked system
7. Cost–_____ relationship must be favourable

Down:

1. Managers need _____ over operations to authorize transactions and safeguard assets
3. Programs that drive a computer
4. Electronic computer equipment
5. A _____ible information system accommodates changes as the organization evolves
6. The opposite of debits

Starter 7–6 ②

From the list below, identify the headings and the account names of LP Gas Co. Assign an account number to each account.

Assets   _____

Current Assets   _____

Inventory   _____

Accounts Payable _____

LP, Capital   _____

LP, Withdrawals   _____

Revenues   _____

Selling Expenses _____

Numbers from which to choose:

151	301
191	311
201	411
281	531

Starter 7–14 ③ ④ ⑤

Use the following abbreviations to indicate the journal in which you would record transactions a through o:

G = General journal   P = Purchases journal

S = Sales journal   CP = Cash payments journal

CR = Cash receipts journal

Transactions:

a. _____ Cash sale of inventory

b. _____ Payment of rent

c. _____ Amortization of computer equipment

d. _____ Purchases of inventory on account

e. _____ Collection of accounts receivable

f. _____ Expiration of prepaid insurance

g. _____ Sale on account

h. _____ Payment on account

i. _____ Cash purchase of inventory

j. _____ Collection of dividend revenue earned on an investment

k. _____ Prepayment of insurance

l. _____ Borrowing money on a long-term note payable

m. _____ Purchase of equipment on account

n. _____ Cost of goods sold along with a credit sale

o. _____ Return of merchandise

*Starter 7–17 ③ ④ Ⓐ①

Answer the following questions about Slopes Ski Shop's special journals.

1. Refer to Slopes Ski Shop's sales journal in Exhibit 7–6 on page 387. How would it look different if Slopes used the periodic inventory system and all credit sales transactions were subject to PST and GST? Give the headings for all new columns.

2. Refer to Slopes Ski Shop's cash receipts journal in Exhibit 7–8 on page 390. How would it look different if Slopes used the periodic inventory system and all cash sales transactions were subject to PST and GST? Give the headings for all new columns.

3. Refer to Slopes Ski Shop's purchases journal in Exhibit 7–9 on page 394. How would it look different if Slopes used the periodic inventory system and all purchases on account were subject to GST? Give the headings for all new columns.

4. Refer to Slopes Ski Shop's cash payments journal in Exhibit 7–10 on page 397. How would it look different if Slopes used the periodic inventory system and most cash payments were subject to GST? Give the headings for all new columns.

Note: You do not need to refer to your textbook. The parts of the Exhibits required to answer the questions have been included.

Requirement 1

EXHIBIT 7–6 | Sales Journal (Panel A)

Panel A: Sales Journal

The check mark indicates that this transaction has been posted to the subledger.

This account is only used for perpetual inventory systems.

Sales Journal — Page 3

Date	Invoice No.	Account Debited	Post. Ref	Accounts Receivable Dr Sales Revenue Cr	Cost of Goods Sold Dr Inventory Cr
2017					
Nov. 2	422	Claudette Cabot 115009	✓	935	505
13	423	Brent Harmon 115115	✓	694	361
18	424	Susan Levy 115249	✓	907	517
27	425	Clay Schmidt 115391	✓	1,783	431
30		Total		4,319	1,814
				(115/410)	511/131

GJ entry:
COGS 505
Inven. 505

GJ entry:
A/R 935
Sales 935

Requirement 2

EXHIBIT 7–8 | Cash Receipts Journal (Panel A)

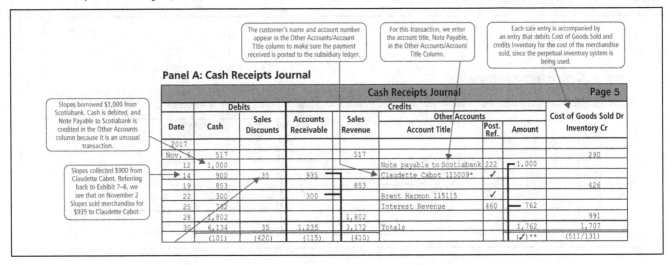

Panel A: Cash Receipts Journal

> The customer's name and account number appear in the Other Accounts/Account Title column to make sure the payment received is posted to the subsidiary ledger.

> For this transaction, we enter the account title, Note Payable, in the Other Accounts/Account Title Column.

> Each sale entry is accompanied by an entry that debits Cost of Goods Sold and credits Inventory for the cost of the merchandise sold, since the perpetual inventory system is being used.

> Slopes borrowed $1,000 from Scotiabank. Cash is debited, and Note Payable to Scotiabank is credited in the Other Accounts column because it is an unusual transaction.

> Slopes collected $900 from Claudette Cabot. Referring back to Exhibit 7–6, we see that on November 2 Slopes sold merchandise for $935 to Claudette Cabot.

		Debits			Credits				
						Other Accounts			**Cost of Goods Sold Dr**
Date	Cash	Sales Discounts	Accounts Receivable	Sales Revenue	Account Title	Post. Ref.	Amount		Inventory Cr
2017									
Nov. 6	517			517					290
12	1,000				Note payable to Scotiabank	222	1,000		
14	900	35	935		Claudette Cabot 115009*	✓			
19	853			853					426
22	300		300		Brent Harmon 115115	✓			
25	762				Interest Revenue	460	762		
28	1,802			1,802					991
30	6,134	35	1,235	3,172	Totals		1,762		1,707
	(101)	(420)	(115)	(410)			(✓)**		(511/131)

Requirement 3

EXHIBIT 7–9 | Purchases Journal (Panel A)

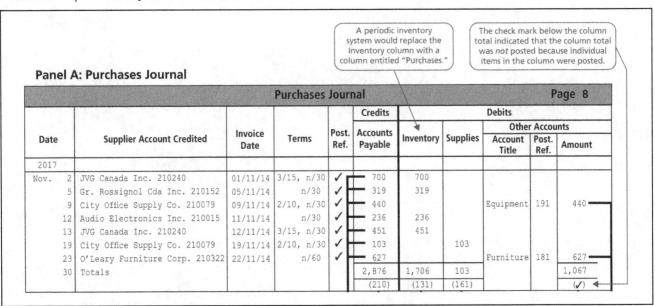

Panel A: Purchases Journal

> A periodic inventory system would replace the Inventory column with a column entitled "Purchases."

> The check mark below the column total indicated that the column total was *not* posted because individual items in the column were posted.

					Credits	Debits				
								Other Accounts		
Date	Supplier Account Credited	Invoice Date	Terms	Post. Ref.	Accounts Payable	Inventory	Supplies	Account Title	Post. Ref.	Amount
2017										
Nov. 2	JVG Canada Inc. 210240	01/11/14	3/15, n/30	✓	700	700				
5	Gr. Rossignol Cda Inc. 210152	05/11/14	n/30	✓	319	319				
9	City Office Supply Co. 210079	09/11/14	2/10, n/30	✓	440			Equipment	191	440
12	Audio Electronics Inc. 210015	11/11/14	n/30	✓	236	236				
13	JVG Canada Inc. 210240	12/11/14	3/15, n/30	✓	451	451				
19	City Office Supply Co. 210079	19/11/14	2/10, n/30	✓	103		103			
23	O'Leary Furniture Corp. 210322	22/11/14	n/60	✓	627			Furniture	181	627
30	Totals				2,876	1,706	103			1,067
					(210)	(131)	(161)			(✓)

Requirement 4

EXHIBIT 7–10 | Cash Payments Journal (Panel A)

> If using a periodic inventory system the only difference in the cash payments journal would be a heading for Purchase Discounts instead of inventory.

Panel A: Cash Payments Journal

					Cash Payments Journal				Page 6
						Debits		**Credits**	
Date	Ch. No.	Payee	Account Debited	Post. Ref.	Other Accounts	Accounts Payable	Inventory	Cash
2017								
Nov. 3	101	R. Landis Ltd.	Rent Expense	541	1,200			1,200
8	102	Grand and Toy	Supplies	161	61			61
15	103	JVG Canada Inc.	JVG Canada Inc. 210240	✓		700	21	679
20	104	Gr. Rossignol Cda Inc.	Gr. Rossignol Cda Inc. 210152	✓		119		119
26	105	Yu Supplies Ltd.	Inventory	131	2,200			2,200
30			Totals		3,461	819	21	4,259
					(✓)	(210)	(131)	(101)

Exercise 7–2 ②

It is very important to set up a properly numbered chart of accounts, especially in a computerized accounting system. Use account numbers 101 through 106, 201, 221, 301, 321, 401, 501, and 521 to correspond to the following selected accounts from the general ledger of Welluck Map Company. List the accounts and their account numbers in proper order, starting with the most liquid current asset.

Randy Welluck, Capital	Amortization Expense—Computer Equipment
Accounts Receivable	Cost of Goods Sold
Cash	Note Payable, Long-Term
Accounts Payable	Randy Welluck, Withdrawals
Computer Equipment	Inventory
Supplies	Sales Revenue
Accumulated Amortization—Computer Equipment	

NUMBER   ACCOUNT

_____

_____

_____

_____

_____

_____

_____

_____

_____

_____

_____

_____

_____

_____

_____

_____

_____

_____

_____

_____

Exercise 7–7 ③

During February, Bryant Corporation had the following transactions:

Feb. 1   Sold merchandise inventory on account to Curtis Co., $1,025.
        Cost of goods, $780. Invoice no. 401.

    6   Sold merchandise inventory for cash, $860 (cost, $640).

  12   Collected interest revenue of $80.

  15   Received cash from Curtis Co. in full settlement of its account receivable. There was no discount.

  20   Sold merchandise inventory on account to Delgado Co., issuing invoice no. 402 for $440 (cost, $330).

  22   Sold merchandise inventory for cash, $560 (cost $420).

  26   Sold office supplies to an employee for cash of $80.

  28   Received $431 from Delgado Co. in full settlement of its account receivable. Delgado earned a discount by paying early. Terms are 2/10, n/15.

Required

1. Prepare headings for the company's sales journal. Journalize the transactions that should be recorded in the sales journal. (Round the sales discount to a whole dollar.) Assume the company uses a perpetual inventory system.
2. Total each column of the sales journal.

Requirements 1 & 2

Sales Journal						PAGE
DATE	INVOICE NO.	ACCOUNT DEBITED	POST REF.	ACCOUNT RECEIVABLE DR. SALES REVENUE CR.	COST OF GOODS SOLD DR. INVENTORY CR.	

Exercise 7–8 ③

Refer to the information in Exercise 7–7.

Required

1. Prepare headings for a cash receipts journal. Journalize the transactions that should be recorded in the cash receipts journal.
2. Total each column of the cash receipts journal.

Cash Receipts Journal

PAGE

DATE	DEBITS			CREDITS				
	CASH	SALES DISCOUNTS	ACCOUNTS RECEIVABLE	SALES REVENUE	OTHER ACCOUNTS			COST OF GOODS SOLD DR. INVENTORY CR.
					ACCOUNT TITLE	POST REF.	AMOUNT	

Exercise 7–9 ③

M and N Sporting Goods reported these selected transactions for the month of July:

Jul.   9   Issued invoice no. 159 for a sale on account to Evans Company, $4,600, terms 1/10, n/30. The cost of the merchandise was $2,700.

      10   Issued invoice no. 160 for a sale on account to Sails and Boats, $5,700, terms 2/15, n/45. The cost of the merchandise was $2,450.

      12   Sold $3,000 of merchandise to Bruce Services for cash. The cost of the merchandise was $1,250.

      16   Owner invested $3,400 into the business.

      18   Collected $580 from Lucille Adams on account.

      20   Issued a credit memo to Sails and Boats for $2,800 for merchandise returned. The cost of the returned merchandise was $1,200.

Required   Record the above transactions in either the sales journal, the cash receipts journal, or the general journal, using Exhibits 7–6 and 7–8 as templates. M and N Sporting Goods uses a perpetual inventory system.

Sales Journal

DATE	ACCOUNT DEBITED	POST REF.	ACCOUNT RECEIVABLE DR. SALES REVENUE CR.	COST OF GOODS SOLD DR. INVENTORY CR.

General Journal

DATE	ACCOUNT TITLES AND EXPLANATIONS	POST REF.	DEBIT	CREDIT

Cash Receipts Journal

PAGE

DATE	DEBITS		CREDITS					
	CASH	SALES DISCOUNTS	ACCOUNTS RECEIVABLE	SALES REVENUE	OTHER ACCOUNTS			COST OF GOODS SOLD DR. INVENTORY CR.
					ACCOUNT TITLE	POST REF.	AMOUNT	

Exercise 7–13 ④

During February, Dean Products had the following transactions:

Feb.   3   Paid $490 on account to Marquis Corp. net of a $10 discount for an earlier purchase of inventory.

6   Purchased inventory for cash, $3,800.

11   Paid $300 cash for supplies.

15   Purchased inventory on account from Monroe Corporation, $1,548.

16   Paid $24,100 on account to LaGrange Ltd.; there was no discount.

21   Purchased furniture for cash, $2,800.

26   Paid $3,900 on account to Graff Software Ltd. for an earlier $4,000 purchase of inventory. The purchase discount was $100.

28   Made a semi-annual interest payment of $2,400 on a long-term note payable. The entire payment was for interest. (Assume none of the interest had been accrued previously.)

Required

1. Prepare a cash payments journal similar to the one illustrated in this chapter. Omit the payee column.

2. Record the transactions in the cash payments journal. Which transaction should not be recorded in the cash payments journal? In what journal does it belong?

3. Total the amount columns of the cash payments journal. Determine that the total debits equal the total credits.

Cash Payments Journal

PAGE

DATE	CHQ. NO.	ACCOUNT DEBITED	POST REF.	DEBITS		CREDITS	
				OTHER ACCOUNTS	ACCOUNTS PAYABLE	INVENTORY	CASH

Exercise 7–16 ④ ⑤

During April, Xitang Company completed the following credit purchase transactions:

Apr. 5   Purchased supplies, $400, from Central Co.

11   Purchased inventory, $1,200, from McDonald Ltd. Xitang Company uses a perpetual inventory system.

14   Issued cheque to pay Central Co.

19   Purchased equipment, $4,300, from Baker Corp.

20   Issued cheque to pay Baker Corp.

22   Purchased inventory, $2,210, from Khalil Inc.

Required   Record these transactions first in the general journal—with explanations—and then in the purchases journal. Omit credit terms, posting references, and invoice dates. After setting up the purchases journal form, which procedure for recording transactions is quicker? Why?

DATE	ACCOUNT TITLES AND EXPLANATIONS	POST REF.	DEBIT	CREDIT

General Journal

Purchases Journal

PAGE

					CREDITS			DEBITS		
									OTHER ACCOUNTS	
DATE	ACCOUNT CREDITED	INV. DATE	TERMS	POST REF.	ACCOUNTS PAYABLE	INVENTORY	SUPPLIES	ACCOUNT TITLE	POST REF.	AMOUNT

Exercise 7–20 ③ ④ ⑤

Lee Management Consulting had the following post-closing trial balance at June 30, 2016. Also shown are the account numbers for each account, including the revenue and expense accounts.

	LEE MANAGEMENT CONSULTING		
	Post-Closing Trial Balance		
	June 30, 2016		
101	Cash	$23,750	
102	Accounts receivable	1,900	
103	Inventory	0	
104	Supplies	100	
105	Prepaid rent	0	
110	Equipment	1,000	
115	Accumulated amortization—equipment		$ 42
120	Furniture	5,000	
125	Accumulated amortization—furniture		167
201	Accounts payable		5,000
202	Salary payable		500
205	Unearned revenue		1,200
301	Michael Lee, capital		24,841
302	Michael Lee, withdrawals		
401	Service revenue		
402	Sales revenue		
501	Cost of goods sold		
511	Rent expense		
513	Utilities expense		
515	Salary expense		
521	Amortization expense—equipment		
522	Amortization expense—furniture		
530	Supplies expense		
	Total	$31,750	$31,750

Consider the July 2016 transactions for Lee Management Consulting that are shown below that were presented in Chapter 6. Cost of goods sold, which was calculated using the moving-weighted-average-cost method in a perpetual inventory system, is shown in brackets after each sale.

Jul. 2 Completed a consulting engagement and received cash of $7,200.

2 Prepaid three months' office rent, $9,000.

7 Purchased 100 units of software inventory on account, $1,900, plus owed the manufacturer freight-in of $100.

16 Paid employee salary, $2,000. (Note previous year-end accrual of $500.)

18 Sold 70 software units on account, $3,100 (cost, $1,400).

19 Consulted with a client for a fee of $900 on account.

21 Paid on account, $2,000, for the July 7 purchase.

22 Purchased 200 units of software inventory on account, $4,600.

24 Paid utilities, $300 cash.

28 Sold 100 units of software for cash, $4,000 (cost, $2,261).

31 Recorded the following adjusting entries:

Accrued salary expense, $1,000.

Prepaid rent used, $3,000.

Amortization of office furniture, $167, and of equipment, $42.

Physical count of inventory, 120 units, $2,713.

Required

1. Open three-column ledger accounts for all the accounts listed in the June 30, 2016, post-closing trial balance, and for the withdrawals, revenue, and expense accounts listed below it. Use the account numbers shown. Insert the June 30, 2016, balances as the opening balances for July 1, 2016.

2. Journalize the July 2016 transactions in the following special journals: cash receipts journal (Page 1), cash payments journal (Page 1), sales journal (Page 1), purchases journal (Page 1), and general journal (Page 6). Total each special journal at July 31, 2016.

3. Post the special journals totals to the three-column ledger accounts using the special journal posting references used in this chapter.

4. Prepare a trial balance in the Trial Balance columns of a worksheet. Record the July 31, 2016, adjusting entries on the worksheet, then complete the Adjusted Trial Balance columns of the worksheet for the month ended July 31, 2016.

5. Journalize and post the adjusting entries. Explanations are not required.

Requirement 2

Sales Journal

PAGE 1

DATE	ACCOUNT DEBITED	INVOICE NO.	POST REF.	ACCOUNTS RECEIVABLE DR.	SERVICE REVENUE CR.	SALES REVENUE CR.	COST OF GOODS SOLD DR. INVENTORY CR.

Cash Receipt Journal

PAGE

	DEBITS		CREDITS		OTHER ACCOUNTS			
DATE	CASH	ACCOUNTS RECEIVABLE	SALES REVENUE	SERVICE REVENUE	ACCOUNT TITLE	POST REF.	AMOUNT	COST OF GOODS SOLD DR. INVENTORY CR.

Requirement 2 (Continued)

Purchases Journal

PAGE

					CREDITS	DEBITS			
								OTHER ACCOUNTS	
DATE	ACCOUNT CREDITED	INV. DATE	TERMS	POST REF.	ACCOUNTS PAYABLE	INVENTORY	ACCOUNT TITLE	POST REF.	AMOUNT

Cash Payments Journal

PAGE

				CREDITS			DEBITS	
DATE	CHQ. NO.	ACCOUNT DEBITED	POST REF.	OTHER ACCOUNTS	ACCOUNTS PAYABLE	SALARY PAYABLE	INVENTORY	CASH

Requirement 3

General Ledger

ACCOUNT	CASH					ACCOUNT NO. 101
DATE		ITEM	JRNL. REF.	DEBIT	CREDIT	BALANCE
Jul.	1		Bal.			23,750 (Dr)

ACCOUNT	ACCOUNTS RECEIVABLE					ACCOUNT NO. 102
DATE		ITEM	JRNL. REF.	DEBIT	CREDIT	BALANCE
Jul.	1		Bal.			1,900 (Dr)

ACCOUNT	INVENTORY					ACCOUNT NO. 103
DATE		ITEM	JRNL. REF.	DEBIT	CREDIT	BALANCE
Jul.	1		Bal.			0

ACCOUNT	SUPPLIES					ACCOUNT NO. 104
DATE		ITEM	JRNL. REF.	DEBIT	CREDIT	BALANCE
Jul.	1		Bal.			100 (Dr)

Requirement 3 (Continued)

General Ledger

ACCOUNT	PREPAID RENT				ACCOUNT NO. 105
DATE	ITEM	JRNL. REF.	DEBIT	CREDIT	BALANCE
Jul. 1		Bal.			0

ACCOUNT	EQUIPMENT				ACCOUNT NO. 110
DATE	ITEM	JRNL. REF.	DEBIT	CREDIT	BALANCE
Jul. 1		Bal.			1,000 (Dr)

ACCOUNT	ACCUMULATED AMORTIZATION—EQUIPMENT				ACCOUNT NO. 115
DATE	ITEM	JRNL. REF.	DEBIT	CREDIT	BALANCE
Jul. 1		Bal.			42 (Cr)

ACCOUNT	FURNITURE				ACCOUNT NO. 120
DATE	ITEM	JRNL. REF.	DEBIT	CREDIT	BALANCE
Jul. 1		Bal.			5,000 (Dr)

Requirement 3 (Continued)

General Ledger

ACCOUNT	ACCUMULATED AMORTIZATION—FURNITURE				ACCOUNT NO. 125	
DATE		ITEM	JRNL. REF.	DEBIT	CREDIT	BALANCE
Jul.	1		Bal.			167 (Cr)

ACCOUNT	ACCOUNTS PAYABLE				ACCOUNT NO. 201	
DATE		ITEM	JRNL. REF.	DEBIT	CREDIT	BALANCE
Jul.	1		Bal.			5,000 (Cr)

ACCOUNT	SALARY PAYABLE				ACCOUNT NO. 202	
DATE		ITEM	JRNL. REF.	DEBIT	CREDIT	BALANCE
Jul.	1		Bal.			500 (Cr)

ACCOUNT	UNEARNED REVENUE				ACCOUNT NO. 205	
DATE		ITEM	JRNL. REF.	DEBIT	CREDIT	BALANCE
Jul.	1		Bal.			1,200 (Cr)

Requirement 3 (Continued)

General Ledger

ACCOUNT	MICHAEL LEE, CAPITAL					ACCOUNT NO. 301
DATE		ITEM	JRNL. REF.	DEBIT	CREDIT	BALANCE
Jul.	1		Bal.			24,841 (Cr)

ACCOUNT	MICHAEL LEE, WITHDRAWALS					ACCOUNT NO. 302
DATE		ITEM	JRNL. REF.	DEBIT	CREDIT	BALANCE
Jul.	1		Bal.			0

ACCOUNT	SERVICE REVENUE					ACCOUNT NO. 401
DATE		ITEM	JRNL. REF.	DEBIT	CREDIT	BALANCE

ACCOUNT	SALES REVENUE					ACCOUNT NO. 402
DATE		ITEM	JRNL. REF.	DEBIT	CREDIT	BALANCE

Requirement 3 (Continued)

General Ledger

ACCOUNT	COST OF GOODS SOLD				ACCOUNT NO. 501
DATE	ITEM	JRNL. REF.	DEBIT	CREDIT	BALANCE

ACCOUNT	RENT EXPENSE				ACCOUNT NO. 511
DATE	ITEM	JRNL. REF.	DEBIT	CREDIT	BALANCE

ACCOUNT	UTILITIES EXPENSE				ACCOUNT NO. 513
DATE	ITEM	JRNL. REF.	DEBIT	CREDIT	BALANCE

ACCOUNT	SALARY EXPENSE				ACCOUNT NO. 515
DATE	ITEM	JRNL. REF.	DEBIT	CREDIT	BALANCE

Requirement 3 (Continued)

General Ledger

ACCOUNT	AMORTIZATION EXPENSE—EQUIPMENT				ACCOUNT NO. 521
DATE	ITEM	JRNL. REF.	DEBIT	CREDIT	BALANCE

ACCOUNT	AMORTIZATION EXPENSE—FURNITURE				ACCOUNT NO. 522
DATE	ITEM	JRNL. REF.	DEBIT	CREDIT	BALANCE

ACCOUNT	SUPPLIES EXPENSE				ACCOUNT NO. 530
DATE	ITEM	JRNL. REF.	DEBIT	CREDIT	BALANCE

Requirement 4

LEE MANAGEMENT CONSULTING
Worksheet
For the Month Ended July 31, 2016

ACCOUNT TITLE	UNADJUSTED TRIAL BALANCE		ADJUSTMENTS		ADJUSTED TRIAL BALANCE	
	DEBIT	CREDIT	DEBIT	CREDIT	DEBIT	CREDIT
Cash						
Accounts receivable						
Inventory						
Supplies						
Prepaid rent						
Equipment						
Accumulated Amortization—equipment						
Furniture						
Accumulated Amortization—furniture						
Accounts payable						
Salary payable						
Unearned revenue						
Michael Lee, capital						
Michael Lee, withdrawals						
Service revenue						
Sales revenue						
Cost of goods sold						
Rent expense						
Utilities expense						
Salary expense						
Amortization expense—equipment						
Amortization expense—furniture						
Supplies expense						

Requirement 5

		General Journal			PAGE 6	
DATE		ACCOUNT TITLES AND EXPLANATIONS	POST REF.	DEBIT		CREDIT

Problem 7–4A ③④⑤

McMillan Distributors, which uses the perpetual inventory system and makes all credit sales on terms of 2/10, n/30, completed the following transactions during July. McMillan records all sales returns and all purchase returns in the general journal.

Jul. 2   Issued invoice no. 913 for sale on account to Teranishi Inc., $12,300. McMillan's cost of this inventory was $5,400.

3   Purchased inventory on credit terms of 3/10, n/60 from Chicosky Corp., $7,401. The invoice was dated July 3.

5   Sold inventory for cash, $3,231 (cost, $1,440).

5   Issued cheque no. 532 to purchase furniture for cash, $6,555.

8   Collected interest revenue of $3,325.

9   Issued invoice no. 914 for sale on account to Bell Ltd., $16,650 (cost, $6,930).

10   Purchased inventory for cash, $3,429, issuing cheque no. 533.

12   Received cash from Teranishi Inc. in full settlement of its account receivable from the sale on July 2.

13   Issued cheque no. 534 to pay Chicosky Corp. the net amount owed from July 3.

13   Purchased supplies on account from Manley Inc., $4,323. Terms were net end of month. The invoice was dated July 12.

15   Sold inventory on account to M. O. Brown, issuing invoice no. 915 for $1,995 (cost, $720).

17   Issued credit memo to M. O. Brown for $1,995 for merchandise sent in error and returned by Brown. Also accounted for receipt of the inventory.

18   Issued invoice no. 916 for credit sale to Teranishi Inc., $1,071 (cost, $381).

19   Received $16,317 from Bell Ltd. in full settlement of its account receivable from July 9.

20   Purchased inventory on credit terms of net 30 from Burgess Distributing Ltd., $6,141. The invoice was dated July 20.

22   Purchased furniture on credit terms of 3/10, n/60 from Chicosky Corp., $1,935. The invoice was dated July 22.

22   Issued cheque no. 535 to pay for insurance coverage, debiting Prepaid Insurance for $3,000.

24   Sold supplies to an employee for cash of $162, which was the cost of the supplies.

25   Issued cheque no. 536 to pay utilities, $3,359

28   Purchased inventory on credit terms of 2/10, n/30 from Manley Inc., $4,025. The invoice was dated July 28.

29   Returned damaged inventory to Manley Inc., issuing a debit memo for $2,025.

29   Sold goods on account to Bell Ltd., issuing invoice no. 917 for $1,488 (cost, $660).

30   Issued cheque no. 537 to pay Manley Inc. $1,323.

31   Received cash in full on account from Teranishi Inc.

31   Issued cheque no. 538 to pay monthly salaries of $7,041.

Required   Use the following abbreviations to indicate the journal in which you would record each of the July transactions. Key each transaction by date. Also indicate whether the transaction would be recorded in the accounts receivable subsidiary ledger or the accounts payable subsidiary ledger.

G = General journal   A/R = accounts receivable subsidiary ledger
P = Purchases journal   A/P = accounts payable subsidiary ledger
S = Sales journal
CP = Cash payments journal
CR = Cash receipts journal

Date	Journal	Subsidiary Ledger
July 2	————	————
3	————	————
5	————	————
5	————	————
8	————	————
9	————	————
10	————	————
12	————	————
13	————	————
13	————	————
15	————	————
17	————	————
18	————	————
19	————	————
20	————	————
22	————	————
22	————	————
24	————	————
25	————	————
28	————	————
29	————	————
29	————	————
30	————	————
31	————	————
31	————	————

Problem 7–5A ③ ⑤

The general ledger of Cannin Distributors includes the following selected accounts, along with their account numbers:

Cash..	11	Land	18
Accounts Receivable.....................	12	Sales Revenue	41
Inventory.......................................	13	Sales Discounts.............................	42
Notes Receivable	15	Sales Returns and Allowances	43
Supplies	16	Cost of Goods Sold........................	51

All credit sales are on the company's standard terms of 2/10, n/30. Transactions in July that affected sales and cash receipts were as follows:

Jul.		
	2	Sold inventory on credit to Fortin Inc., $2,800. Cannin's cost of these goods was $1,600.
	4	As a favour to a competitor, sold supplies at cost, $3,400, receiving cash.
	7	Cash sales of merchandise for the week totalled $7,560 (cost, $6,560).
	9	Sold merchandise on account to A. L. Price, $29,280 (cost, $20,440).
	10	Sold land that cost $50,000 for cash of $50,000.
	11	Sold goods on account to Sloan Forge Ltd., $20,416 (cost, $14,080).
	12	Received cash from Fortin Inc. in full settlement of its account receivable from July 2.
	14	Cash sales of merchandise for the week were $8,424 (cost, $6,120).
	15	Sold inventory on credit to the partnership of Wilkie & Blinn, $14,600 (cost, $9,040).
	18	Received inventory sold on July 9 to A. L. Price for $2,400. The goods shipped were the wrong size. These goods cost Cannin $1,760.
	20	Sold merchandise on account to Sloan Forge Ltd., $2,516 (cost, $1,800).
	21	Cash sales of merchandise for the week were $3,960 (cost, $2,760).
	22	Received $8,000 cash from A. L. Price in partial settlement of his account receivable.
	25	Received cash from Wilkie & Blinn for its account receivable from July 15.
	25	Sold goods on account to Olsen Inc., $6,080 (cost, $4,200).
	27	Collected $10,500 on a note receivable.
	28	Cash sales of merchandise for the week were $15,096 (cost, $9,840).
	29	Sold inventory on account to R. O. Bankston Inc., $968 (cost, $680).
	30	Received goods sold on July 25 to Olsen Inc. for $160. The wrong items were shipped. The cost of the goods was $100.
	31	Received $18,880 cash on account from A. L. Price.

Required

1. Use the appropriate journal to record the above transactions: a sales journal (omit the Invoice No. column), a cash receipts journal, or a general journal. Cannin Distributors records sales returns and allowances in the general journal.
2. Total each column of the sales journal and the cash receipts journal. Show that total debits equal total credits.
3. Show how postings would be made from the journals by writing the account numbers and check marks in the appropriate places in the journals.

Requirements 1 – 3

Sales Journal

DATE		ACCOUNTS DEBITED	POST REF.	ACCOUNTS RECEIVABLE DR. SALES REVENUE CR.	COST OF GOODS SOLD DR. INVENTORY CR.

General Journal

DATE		ACCOUNT TITLES AND EXPLANATIONS	POST REF.	DEBIT	CREDIT

Requirements 1 – 3 (Continued)

Cash Receipts Journal

PAGE

DATE	DEBITS			CREDITS					
	CASH	SALES DISCOUNTS	ACCOUNTS RECEIVABLE	SALES REVENUE	OTHER ACCOUNTS			COST OF GOODS SOLD DR. INVENTORY CR.
					ACCOUNT TITLE	POST REF.	AMOUNT	

Problem 7–6A ④ ⑤

The general ledger of Katie's Supplies includes the following accounts:

Cash............	111	Furniture............	187
Inventory............	131	Accounts Payable............	211
Prepaid Insurance............	161	Rent Expense............	564
Supplies............	171	Utilities Expense............	583

Transactions in August that affected purchases and cash payments were as follows:

Aug. 1   Purchased inventory on credit from Stiples Corp., $6,900. Terms were 2/10, n/30. The invoice was dated August 1.

     1   Paid monthly rent, debiting Rent Expense for $2,000.

     5   Purchased supplies on credit terms of 2/10, n/30 from Bella Supply Ltd., $450. The invoice date was August 5.

     8   Paid electricity bill, $600.

     9   Purchased furniture on account from Rite Office Supply, $9,100. Payment terms were net 30. The invoice date was August 8.

     10   Returned the furniture to Rite Office Supply. It was the wrong colour.

     11   Paid Stiples Corp. the amount owed on the purchase of August 1.

     12   Purchased inventory on account from Wynne Inc., $4,400. Terms were 3/10, n/30. The invoice was dated August 12.

     13   Purchased inventory for cash, $650.

     14   Paid a semi-annual insurance premium, debiting Prepaid Insurance, $1,200.

     15   Paid the account payable to Bella Supply Ltd. from August 5.

     18   Paid gas and water bills with cash, $100.

     21   Purchased inventory on credit terms of 1/10, n/45 from Cyber Software Ltd., $5,200. The invoice was dated August 21.

     21   Paid account payable to Wynne Inc. from August 12.

     22   Purchased supplies on account from Favron Sales, $2,740. Terms were net 30. The invoice was dated August 21.

     25   Returned $1,200 of the inventory purchased on August 21 to Cyber Software Ltd.

     31   Paid Cyber Software Ltd. the net amount owed from August 21.

Required

1. Katie's Supplies records purchase returns in the general journal. Use the appropriate journal to record the above transactions: a purchases journal, a cash payments journal (omit the Cheque No. column), or a general journal.

2. Total each column of the special journals. Show that total debits equal total credits in each journal.

3. Show how postings would be made from the journals by writing the account numbers and check marks in the appropriate places in the journals.

Requirement 1

General Journal				
DATE	ACCOUNT TITLES AND EXPLANATIONS	POST REF.	DEBIT	CREDIT

Requirements 1 – 3

Purchases Journal

PAGE _____

DATE	ACCOUNT CREDITED	INV. DATE	TERMS	POST REF.	CREDITS ACCOUNTS PAYABLE	DEBITS INVENTORY	SUPPLIES	OTHER ACCOUNTS ACCOUNT TITLE	POST REF.	AMOUNT

Requirements 1 – 3 (Continued)

Cash Payments Journal

PAGE

DATE	CHQ. NO.	ACCOUNT DEBITED	POST REF.	DEBITS		CREDITS	
				OTHER ACCOUNTS	ACCOUNTS PAYABLE	INVENTORY	CASH

Problem 7–7A ③ ④ ⑤

Callahan Distributors, which uses the perpetual inventory system and makes all credit sales on terms of 1/10, n/30, completed the following transactions during July:

Jul. 2 Issued invoice no. 913 for sale on account to Ishikawa Inc., $24,600. Callahan's cost of this inventory was $10,800. Credit sales terms are 1/10, n/30.

3 Purchased inventory on credit terms of 3/10, n/60 from Nakkach Corp., $14,802. The invoice was dated July 3.

5 Sold inventory for cash, $6,462 (cost, $2,880).

5 Issued cheque no. 532 to purchase furniture for cash, $13,110.

8 Collected interest revenue of $6,650.

9 Issued invoice no. 914 for sale on account to Bell Ltd., $33,300 (cost, $13,860). Credit sales terms are 1/10, n/30.

10 Purchased inventory for cash, $6,858, issuing cheque no. 533.

12 Received cash from Ishikawa Inc. in full settlement of its account receivable from the sale on July 2.

13 Issued cheque no. 534 to pay Nakkach Corp. the net amount owed from July 3. (Round to the nearest dollar.)

13 Purchased supplies on account from Manley Inc., $8,646. Terms were net end of month. The invoice was dated July 13.

15 Sold inventory on account to M. O. Brown, issuing invoice no. 915 for $3,990 (cost, $1,440). Credit sales terms are 1/10, n/30.

17 Issued credit memo to M. O. Brown for $3,990 for merchandise sent in error and returned by Brown. Also accounted for receipt of the inventory.

18 Issued invoice no. 916 for credit sale to Ishikawa Inc., $2,142 (cost, $762). Credit sales terms are 1/10, n/30.

19 Received $32,967 from Bell Ltd. in full settlement of its account receivable from July 9.

20 Purchased inventory on credit terms of net 30 from Burgess Distributing Ltd., $12,282. The invoice was dated July 20.

22 Purchased furniture on credit terms of 3/10, n/60 from Nakkach Corp., $3,870. The invoice was dated July 22.

22 Issued cheque no. 535 to pay for insurance coverage, debiting Prepaid Insurance for $6,000.

24 Sold supplies to an employee for cash of $324, which was the cost of the supplies.

25 Issued cheque no. 536 to pay utilities, $6,718.

28 Purchased inventory on credit terms of 2/10, n/30 from Manley Inc., $8,050. The invoice date was July 28.

29 Returned damaged inventory to Manley Inc., issuing a debit memo for $4,050.

29 Sold goods on account to Bell Ltd., issuing invoice no. 917 for $2,976 (cost, $1,320). Credit sales terms are 1/10, n/30.

30 Issued cheque no. 537 to pay Manley Inc. $2,646.

31 Received cash in full on account from Ishikawa Inc.

31 Issued cheque no. 538 to pay monthly salaries of $14,082.

Required

1. Open the following three-column general ledger accounts using the account numbers given:

Cash	111	Sales Revenue	411
Accounts Receivable	112	Sales Discounts	412
Supplies	116	Sales Returns and Allowances	413
Prepaid Insurance	117	Interest Revenue	419
Inventory	118	Cost of Goods Sold	511
Furniture	151	Salaries Expense	531
Accounts Payable	211	Utilities Expense	541

2. Open these accounts in the subsidiary ledgers: accounts receivable subsidiary ledger—Bell Ltd., M. O. Brown, and Ishikawa Inc.; accounts payable subsidiary ledger—Nakkach Corp., Manley Inc., and Burgess Distributing Ltd.

3. Enter the transactions in a sales journal (Page 7), a cash receipts journal (Page 5), a purchases journal (Page 10), a cash payments journal (Page 8), and a general journal (Page 6), as appropriate.

4. Post daily to the accounts receivable subsidiary ledger and to the accounts payable subsidiary ledger. Post the individual amounts to the general ledger on the date recorded in the journal; post column totals to the general ledger on July 31.

5. Total each column of the special journals. Show that total debits equal total credits in each journal.

6. Balance or reconcile the accounts receivable subsidiary ledger and Accounts Receivable in the general ledger. Do the same for the accounts payable subsidiary ledger and Accounts Payable in the general ledger.

Requirements 1 & 4 (Posting to Ledgers)

General Ledger

ACCOUNT	CASH					ACCOUNT NO. 111
DATE		ITEM	JRNL. REF.	DEBIT	CREDIT	BALANCE

ACCOUNT	ACCOUNTS RECEIVABLE					ACCOUNT NO. 112
DATE		ITEM	JRNL. REF.	DEBIT	CREDIT	BALANCE

Requirements 1 & 4 (Posting to Ledgers) (Continued)

General Ledger

ACCOUNT	SUPPLIES				ACCOUNT NO. 116
DATE	ITEM	JRNL. REF.	DEBIT	CREDIT	BALANCE

ACCOUNT	PREPAID INSURANCE				ACCOUNT NO. 117
DATE	ITEM	JRNL. REF.	DEBIT	CREDIT	BALANCE

ACCOUNT	INVENTORY				ACCOUNT NO. 118
DATE	ITEM	JRNL. REF.	DEBIT	CREDIT	BALANCE

ACCOUNT	FURNITURE				ACCOUNT NO. 151
DATE	ITEM	JRNL. REF.	DEBIT	CREDIT	BALANCE

Requirements 1 & 4 (Posting to Ledgers) (Continued)

General Ledger

ACCOUNT	ACCOUNTS PAYABLE				ACCOUNT NO. 211
DATE	ITEM	JRNL. REF.	DEBIT	CREDIT	BALANCE

ACCOUNT	SALES REVENUE				ACCOUNT NO. 411
DATE	ITEM	JRNL. REF.	DEBIT	CREDIT	BALANCE

ACCOUNT	SALES DISCOUNTS				ACCOUNT NO. 412
DATE	ITEM	JRNL. REF.	DEBIT	CREDIT	BALANCE

ACCOUNT	SALES RETURNS AND ALLOWANCES				ACCOUNT NO. 413
DATE	ITEM	JRNL. REF.	DEBIT	CREDIT	BALANCE

Requirements 1 & 4 (Posting to Ledgers) (Continued)

General Ledger

ACCOUNT	INTEREST REVENUE				ACCOUNT NO. 419
DATE		ITEM	JRNL. REF.	DEBIT	CREDIT	BALANCE

ACCOUNT	COST OF GOODS SOLD				ACCOUNT NO. 511
DATE		ITEM	JRNL. REF.	DEBIT	CREDIT	BALANCE

ACCOUNT	SALARIES EXPENSE				ACCOUNT NO. 531
DATE		ITEM	JRNL. REF.	DEBIT	CREDIT	BALANCE

ACCOUNT	UTILITIES EXPENSE				ACCOUNT NO. 541
DATE		ITEM	JRNL. REF.	DEBIT	CREDIT	BALANCE

Requirements 2 & 4 (Posting to Ledgers)

Accounts Receivable Subsidiary Ledger

ACCOUNT   BELL LTD.

DATE		ITEM	JRNL. REF.	DEBIT	CREDIT	BALANCE

ACCOUNT   M.O. BROWN

DATE		ITEM	JRNL. REF.	DEBIT	CREDIT	BALANCE

ACCOUNT   ISHIKAWA INC.

DATE		ITEM	JRNL. REF.	DEBIT	CREDIT	BALANCE

ACCOUNT   BURGESS DISTRIBUTING LTD.

DATE		ITEM	JRNL. REF.	DEBIT	CREDIT	BALANCE

Requirements 2 & 4 (Posting to Ledgers) (Continued)

Accounts Receivable Subsidiary Ledger

ACCOUNT   NAKKACH CORP.

DATE		ITEM	JRNL. REF.	DEBIT	CREDIT	BALANCE

ACCOUNT   MANLEY, INC.

DATE		ITEM	JRNL. REF.	DEBIT	CREDIT	BALANCE

Requirements 3 & 5 (Journalizing Transactions)

		Sales Journal				PAGE
DATE		INVOICE NO.	ACCOUNTS DEBITED	POST REF.	ACCOUNTS RECEIVABLE DR. SALES REVENUE CR.	COST OF GOODS SOLD DR. INVENTORY CR.

Requirements 3 & 5 (Journalizing Transactions) (Continued)

Cash Receipts Journal

PAGE

DATE	DEBITS		CREDITS					
	CASH	SALES DISCOUNTS	ACCOUNTS RECEIVABLE	SALES REVENUE	OTHER ACCOUNTS			COST OF GOODS SOLD DR. INVENTORY CR.
					ACCOUNT TITLE	POST REF.	AMOUNT	

Purchases Journal

PAGE

DATE	ACCOUNT CREDITED	INV. DATE	TERMS	POST REF.	CREDITS	DEBITS		OTHER ACCOUNTS		
					ACCOUNTS PAYABLE	INVENTORY	SUPPLIES	ACCOUNT TITLE	POST REF.	AMOUNT

Requirements 3 & 5 (Journalizing Transactions) (Continued)

Cash Payments Journal

PAGE ____

DATE	CHQ. NO.	PAYEE	ACCOUNT DEBITED	POST REF.	DEBITS		CREDITS	
					OTHER ACCOUNTS	ACCOUNTS PAYABLE	INVENTORY	CASH

Requirements 3 & 5 (Journalizing Transactions) (Continued)

General Journal

DATE		ACCOUNT TITLES AND EXPLANATIONS	POST REF.	DEBIT	CREDIT

Requirement 6

8 INTERNAL CONTROL AND CASH

LEARNING OBJECTIVES

1 Define internal control.
2 List and describe the components of internal control and control procedures.
3 Prepare a bank reconciliation and the related journal entries.
4 Apply internal controls to cash receipts and cash payments.
5 Apply internal controls to petty cash.
6 Make ethical business judgments.

Starter 8–3 ①

Explain in your own words why separation of duties is often described as the cornerstone of internal control for safeguarding assets. Describe what can happen if the same person has custody of an asset and also accounts for the asset.

_____

_____

_____

_____

_____

_____

_____

_____

_____

_____

Starter 8–4 ②

How do external auditors differ from internal auditors? How does an external audit differ from an internal audit? How are the two types of audits similar?

_____

_____

_____

_____

_____

_____

_____

_____

_____

_____

Starter 8–14 ⑥

Angela Brennan, an accountant for Dublin Co., discovers that her supervisor, Barney Stone, made several errors last year. Overall, the errors overstated the company's net income by 15 percent. It is not clear whether the errors were deliberate or accidental. What should Brennan do?

_____

_____

_____

_____

_____

_____

_____

_____

_____

_____

_____

Exercise 8–8 ③

The following items could appear on a bank reconciliation:

a. Outstanding cheques

b. Deposits in transit for current month

c. NSF cheque

d. Bank collection of a note receivable on the company's behalf

e. Bank credit memo for interest earned on bank balance

f. Bank debit memo for service charge

g. Book error: We credited Cash for $200. The correct credit was $2,000.

h. Bank error: The bank decreased our account for a cheque written by another customer.

i. Outstanding cheques from the previous month that are still outstanding

j. EFT payment by a customer

k. Bank error in recording a deposit for $464 should have been $446

Required

1. Classify each item as (1) an addition to the book balance, (2) a subtraction from the book balance, (3) an addition to the bank balance, or (4) a subtraction from the bank balance.

2. Indicate (a) the items that will result in an adjustment to the company's records, and (b) why the other items do not require an adjustment.

Requirements 1 & 2a

	Classification of Change (1,2,3, or 4)	Adjustment Required (Y/N)
a.		
b.		
c.		
d.		
e.		
f.		
g.		
h.		
i.		
j.		
k.		

Requirement 2b

Exercise 8–9 ③

Adams Enterprises began operations on January 2, 2017, depositing $40,000 in the bank. During this first month of business, the following transactions occurred that affected the Cash account in the general ledger:

Date		Description	Dr	Cr
Jan.	2	Deposit	$40,000	
	5	Payment, cheque 001		$12,000
	8	Payment, cheque 002		16,000
	9	Cash sales	16,000	
	15	Payment, cheque 003		10,000
	18	Cash sales	12,000	
	20	Bank loan	50,000	
	26	Equipment purchase, cheque 004		74,000
	30	Payment on account, cheque 005		17,000
	31	Cash sales	25,600	

Shortly after the end of January the company received its first bank statement:

Description	Withdrawals	Deposits	Date	Balance
Balance Forward			Jan01	0
Deposit		40,000	Jan02	40,000
Chq#001	12,000		Jan07	28,000
Deposit		16,000	Jan09	44,000
Chq#002	16,000		Jan13	28,000
Deposit		12,000	Jan18	40,000
Bank Loan		50,000	Jan20	90,000
Chq#004	74,000		Jan28	16,000
Deposit		2,000	Jan29	18,000
Service Charge	48		Jan31	17,952
Interest		8	Jan31	17,960
	102,048	120,008		

In preparing to do the bank reconciliation, Adams Enterprises noticed that the $2,000 deposit on January 29 was a bank error and informed the bank. The bank will correct the error on the next bank statement.

Required Prepare Adams Enterprises' bank reconciliation at January 31, 2017.

Exercise 8–10 ③

Inkameep Travel's general ledger Cash account showed the following transactions during October 2017:

Date	Description	Dr	Cr	Balance
Oct. 1	Opening balance			$ 2,800
2	Deposit	$20,000		22,800
5	Payment, cheque 233		$ 6,000	16,800
8	Payment, cheque 234		18,000	(1,200)
9	Deposit	18,000		16,800
15	Payment, cheque 235		5,000	11,800
18	Deposit	5,200		17,000
26	Payment, cheque 236		3,300	13,700
30	Payment, cheque 237		4,750	8,950
31	Deposit	10,500		19,450

The bank statement for the month ending October 31, 2017, is shown below:

Description	Withdrawals	Deposits	Date	Balance
Balance Forward			Oct01	2,800
Deposit		20,000	Oct02	22,800
Chq#00233	6,000		Oct07	16,800
Deposit		18,000	Oct09	34,800
Chq#00234	18,000		Oct10	16,800
Deposit		5,200	Oct18	22,000
Chq#00235	5,000		Oct18	17,000
Service Charge	120		Oct31	16,880
Service Charge	120		Oct31	16,760
Interest		4	Oct31	16,764
	29,240	43,204		

Inkameep Travel informed its bank that the bank charged a service charge twice. The bank has agreed to reverse one of the bank charges on the next month's bank statement.

Required Prepare Inkameep Travel's bank reconciliation at October 31, 2017.

Exercise 8–19 ④

The petty cash fund had the following petty cash ticket:

Toner for a printer...	$ 42
Freight to deliver goods sold...	39
Freight on inventory purchased..	112
Miscellaneous expense..	10
Postage expense..	25
	$228

Assume that the business has established a petty cash fund in the amount of $250 and that the amount of cash in the fund at the time of replenishment is $20. The business uses a perpetual inventory system.

Prepare the entry to replenish the fund on February 28.

General Journal					
DATE	ACCOUNT TITLES AND EXPLANATIONS	POST REF.	DEBIT	CREDIT	

Exercise 8–20 ⑤

Record the following selected transactions of Kelly's Fine Foods in general journal format (explanations are not required):

2017

Jun. 1 Established a petty cash fund with a $200 balance.

2 Journalized the day's cash sales. Cash register tapes show a $4,875 total, but the cash in the register is $4,885.

10 The petty cash fund had $56.50 in cash and $134.00 in petty cash tickets issued to pay for office supplies ($21.00), delivery expenses ($69.50), and entertainment expenses ($43.50). Replenished the fund.

		General Journal		
DATE	ACCOUNT TITLES AND EXPLANATIONS	POST REF.	DEBIT	CREDIT

Exercise 8–22 ⑤

Maritime Distributors created a $500 imprest petty cash fund. During the first month of use, the fund custodian authorized and signed petty cash tickets as shown below.

Ticket No.	Item	Account Debited	Amount
1	Delivery of flyers to customers	Delivery Expense	$228.80
2	Stamp purchase	Postage Expense	85.98
3	Newsletter	Supplies Expense	60.40
4	Key to closet	Miscellaneous Expense	9.52
5	Staples	Supplies Expense	14.72

Required Make general journal entries to (a) create the petty cash fund and (b) record its replenishment. Cash in the fund totals $97.58. Include explanations.

General Journal

DATE	ACCOUNT TITLES AND EXPLANATIONS	POST REF.	DEBIT	CREDIT

Exercise 8–23 ⑤

Refer to the Maritime Distributors petty cash fund data in Exercise 8-22. Suppose, one month later, the company decided to decrease the petty cash fund by $100 due to theft and break-ins in the area. Journalize the decrease in the petty cash fund.

General Journal

DATE	ACCOUNT TITLES AND EXPLANATIONS	POST REF.	DEBIT	CREDIT

Exercise 8–25 ③

Lee Management Consulting performs systems consulting. Lee Management Consulting's bank statement dated October 31, 2016, follows:

Description	Withdrawals	Deposits	Date	Balance
Balance Forward			Sep30	$32,850
Deposit		750*	Oct01	33,600
EFT to Cheap Cheques	17		Oct02	33,583
Chq 206	1,250*		Oct02	32,333
Deposit		2,500	Oct08	34,833
Deposit		3,000	Oct14	37,833
Chq 207	4,000		Oct17	33,833
Chq 209	1,415		Oct18	32,418
EFT Hot Houses (a customer)		500	Oct20	32,918
Deposit		4,800	Oct22	37,718
EFT to Internet Service	125		Oct28	37,593
Chq 208	795		Oct28	36,798
Bank Service Charge	13		Oct28	36,785
Interest Credit		7	Oct31	36,792
	7,615	11,557		

*This was a reconciling item on the September 2016 bank reconciliation.

Lee's October Cash from its general ledger appears below:

Cash

Sep.	30	Bal.	32,350	chq. 207	4,000	Oct.	1
Oct.	6		2,500	chq. 208	795	Oct.	14
Oct.	13		3,000	chq. 209	1,415	Oct.	14
Oct.	20		4,800	chq. 210	190	Oct.	28
Oct.	27		3,600	chq. 211	400	Oct.	28
Oct.	28	Unadj. Bal.	39,450				

Required

1. Prepare the October 2016 bank reconciliation.
2. Journalize and post any transactions required from the bank reconciliation. Key all items by date. Compute each account balance, and denote the balance as *Bal.*

Requirement 1

Requirement 2

	General Journal			
DATE	ACCOUNT TITLES AND EXPLANATIONS	POST REF.	DEBIT	CREDIT

Requirement 2 (Continued)

Cash

Sep. 30	32,350	Oct. 1	4,000
Oct. 6	2,500	Oct. 14	795
Oct. 13	3,000	Oct. 14	1,415
Oct. 20	4,800	Oct. 28	190
Oct. 27	3,600	Oct. 28	400
Unadj. Bal.	39,450		

Problem 8–3A ②

Each of the following situations has an internal control weakness:

a. Syspro Software Associates sells accounting software. Recently, the development of a new software program stopped while the programmers redesigned Syspro Software Associates' accounting system. Syspro Software Associates' own accountants could have performed this task.

b. Judy Sloan has been your trusted employee for 30 years. She performs all cash-handling and accounting duties. She has just purchased a new Lexus and a new home in an expensive suburb. As the owner of the company, you wonder how she can afford these luxuries because you pay her $35,000 per year and she has no sources of outside income.

c. Sanchez Hardwoods Ltd., a private corporation, falsified sales and inventory figures to get a large loan. The company prepared its own financial statements. The company received the loan but later went bankrupt and couldn't repay the loan.

d. The office supply company from which The Family Shoe Store purchases sales receipts recently notified Family that the last shipped receipts were not prenumbered. Louise Bourseault, the owner of Family, replied that she never uses the receipt numbers, so the omission is not important.

e. Discount stores such as Dollar Mart make most of their sales for cash, with the remainder in debit card and credit card sales. To reduce expenses, one store manager ceases purchasing fidelity bonds on the cashiers.

Required

1. Identify the missing internal control characteristic in each situation.
2. Identify the potential problem that could be caused by each control weakness.
3. Propose a solution to each internal control problem.

MISSING INTERNAL CONTROL CHARACTERSTIC	POSSIBLE PROBLEM	SOLUTION

Problem 8–4A ③

The cash receipts and the cash payments of Silver Hills Estates Development for November 2017 are as follows:

Cash Receipts (Posting Reference is CR)

Date	Cash Debit
Nov. 5	$ 3,436
7	470
13	1,723
15	1,065
19	441
24	10,875
30	2,598
Total	$20,608

Cash Payments (Posting Reference is CP)

Cheque No.	Cash Credit
1221	$ 1,819
1222	1,144
1223	429
1224	111
1225	816
1226	109
1227	4,468
1228	998
1229	330
1230	2,724
Total	$12,948

The Cash account of Silver Hills Estates shows a balance of $26,983 on November 30, 2017. Outstanding amounts from the previous month's bank reconciliation were cheque #1219 for $500, cheque #1218 for $400, and an October 31 deposit in the amount of $2,000. On December 3, 2017, Silver Hills Estates received this bank statement:

Bank Statement for November 2017				
Description	Withdrawals	Deposits	Date	Balance
Balance Forward			Nov01	18,223
Deposit		2,000	Nov01	20,223
EFT Rent Collection		880	Nov01	21,103
Deposit		3,436	Nov06	24,539
NSF Cheque	433		Nov08	24,106
Chq#001221	1,819		Nov09	22,287
Deposit		470	Nov10	22,757
Chq#001222	1,144		Nov13	21,613
Chq#001223	429		Nov14	21,184
Deposit		1,723	Nov14	22,907
Chq#001224	111		Nov15	22,796
Deposit		1,065	Nov15	23,861
EFT Insurance	275		Nov19	23,586
Deposit		441	Nov20	24,027
Chq#001225	816		Nov22	23,211
Deposit		10,875	Nov25	34,086
Chq#001226	109		Nov29	33,977
Chq#001227	4,968		Nov30	29,009
Bank Collection		1,430	Nov30	30,439
Chq#001219	500		Nov30	29,939
Service Charge	25		Nov30	29,914
	10,629	22,320		

Explanations: EFT—electronic funds transfer, NSF—nonsufficient funds

Additional data for the bank reconciliation is as follows:

a. The EFT deposit was a receipt of monthly rent. The EFT debit was payment for monthly insurance.

b. The NSF cheque was received late in October from a customer.

c. The $1,430 bank collection of a note receivable on November 30 included $100 interest revenue.

d. The correct amount of cheque #1227, a payment on account, is $4,968. (The Silver Hills Estates Development accountant mistakenly recorded the cheque for $4,468.)

Required

1. Prepare the bank reconciliation of Silver Hills Estates Development at November 30, 2017.

2. Describe how a bank account and the bank reconciliation help Silver Hills' managers control the business's cash.

3. How are outstanding items from the previous month's bank reconciliation that clear on the November bank statement dealt with?

Requirement 1

Requirements 2 & 3

_____

_____

_____

_____

_____

_____

Problem 8–5A ③

Spottify Electronics had a computer failure on October 1, 2017, that resulted in the loss of data, including the balance of its Cash account and its bank reconciliation from September 30, 2017. The accountant, Matt Vincent, has been able to obtain the following information from the records of the company and its bank:

a. An examination showed that two cheques (#244 for $305.00 and #266 for $632.50) had not been cashed as of October 1. Vincent recalled that there was only one deposit in transit on the September 30 bank reconciliation but was unable to recall the amount.

b. The cash receipts and cash payments journals contained the following entries for October 2017:

Cash Receipts:		Cash Payments:	
Amounts		**Cheque #**	**Amount**
$ 908.50		275	$ 310.50
1,748.00		276	448.50
3,726.00		277	466.90
1,975.00		278	811.90
736.00		279	577.30
$9,093.50		280	3,886.90
		281	void
		282	488.50
		283	1,058.00
			$8,048.50

c. The company's bank provided the following statement as of October 31, 2017:

Date		Cheques and Other Debits		Deposits and Other Credits	Balance
Oct.	1	#276	448.50	2,346.00	6,520.50
	2	#266	632.50		5,888.00
	5	#277	466.90		5,421.10
	8			908.50	6,329.60
	14	#275	310.50	1,196.00	7,215.10
	17	EFT	529.00		6,686.10
	19			EFT 414.00	7,100.10
	22	#279	577.30	1,748.00	8,270.80
	22	#280	3,976.90	EFT 1,196.00	5,489.90
	24			EFT 471.50	5,961.40
	27	NSF	805.00	3,726.00	8,882.40
	28	SC	20.00		8,862.40
	31	#283	1,058.00	1,975.00	9,779.40

d. The deposit made on October 14 was for the collection of a note receivable ($1,100.00) plus interest.

e. The electronic funds transfers (EFTs) had not yet been recorded by Spottify Electronics because the bank statement was the first notification of them.

  • The October 17 EFT was for the monthly payment on an insurance policy for Spottify Electronics.

  • The October 19 and 24 EFTs were collections on accounts receivable.

  • The October 22 EFT was in error—the transfer should have been to Spottify Auto Parts.

f. The NSF cheque on October 27 was received from a customer as payment for electronics purchased for $805.00.

g. Cheque #280 was correctly written for $3,976.90 for the purchase of inventory (assume a periodic system) but incorrectly recorded by the cash payments clerk.

Required

1. Prepare a bank reconciliation as of October 31, 2017, including the calculation of the book balance of October 31, 2017.

2. Prepare all journal entries that would be required by the bank reconciliation.

Requirement 1

Requirement 2

General Journal

DATE		ACCOUNT TITLES AND EXPLANATIONS	POST REF.	DEBIT	CREDIT

Problem 8–9A ⑤

Suppose that, on June 1, Devine Design creates a petty cash fund with an imprest balance of $400. During June, Lucie Chao, the fund custodian, signs the following petty cash tickets:

Ticket No.	Item	Amount
101	Office supplies	$ 26.64
102	Cab fare for executive	60.00
103	Delivery of package across town	29.32
104	Dinner money for sales manager entertaining a customer	133.34
105	Office supplies	127.20

On June 30, prior to replenishment, the fund contains these tickets plus $34.40. The accounts affected by petty cash payments are Office Supplies Expense, Travel Expense, Delivery Expense, and Entertainment Expense.

Required

1. Explain the characteristics and internal control features of an imprest fund.
2. On June 30, how much cash should the petty cash fund hold before it is replenished?
3. Make general journal entries to (a) create the fund and (b) replenish it. Include explanations.
4. Make the July 1 entry to increase the fund balance to $500. Include an explanation, and briefly describe what the custodian does in this case.

Requirements 1 & 2

Requirement 3a

General Journal

DATE		ACCOUNT TITLES AND EXPLANATIONS	POST REF.	DEBIT	CREDIT

Requirement 3b

General Journal

DATE		ACCOUNT TITLES AND EXPLANATIONS	POST REF.	DEBIT	CREDIT

Requirement 4

General Journal

DATE		ACCOUNT TITLES AND EXPLANATIONS	POST REF.	DEBIT	CREDIT

9 RECEIVABLES

LEARNING OBJECTIVES

1 Define common types of receivables, and report receivables on the balance sheet.
2 Use the allowance method to account for uncollectibles, and estimate uncollectibles by the percent-of-sales, aging-of-accounts-receivable, and the percent-of-accounts receivable methods.
3 Use the direct write-off method to account for uncollectibles.
4 Account for credit card, debit card, and online sales.
5 Account for notes receivable.
6 Use the acid-test ratio and days' sales in receivables to evaluate a company.
7 Understand the impact on accounts receivable of International Financial Reporting Standards (IFRS).

*A1 Discount a note receivable.

Starter 9–5 ③

Tolco Importers Inc. had the following balances at December 31, 2017, before the year-end adjustments:

Accounts Receivable		Allowance for Doubtful Accounts	
148,000			4,000

The aging of accounts receivable yields these data:

	Age of Accounts Receivable		
	0–60 Days	Over 60 Days	Total Receivables
Accounts receivable	$140,000	$8,000	$148,000
Percent uncollectible	3%	20%	

1. Journalize Tolco Importers Inc.'s entry to adjust the Allowance account to its correct balance at December 31, 2017.
2. Prepare the T-account for Allowance for Doubtful Accounts.
3. Repeat question 1 assuming that, instead of aging the accounts, the allowance is calculated as 3.5 percent of the Accounts Receivable balance.

Requirement 1

General Journal				
DATE	ACCOUNT TITLES AND EXPLANATIONS	POST REF.	DEBIT	CREDIT

Requirement 2

Allowance for Doubtful Accounts

Requirement 3

General Journal

DATE	ACCOUNT TITLES AND EXPLANATIONS	POST REF.	DEBIT	CREDIT

Starter 9–8 (3)

University Cycle Shop had trouble collecting its account receivable from Matt Reid. On January 19, University finally wrote off Reid's $2,400 account receivable. University turned the account over to a lawyer, who pursued Reid for payment for the rest of the year. On December 31, Reid sent a $2,400 cheque to University Cycle Shop with a note that said, "Here's your money. Please call off your bloodhound!"

Journalize the following transactions for University Cycle Shop:

Jan.	19	Write-off of Reid's account against Allowance for Doubtful Accounts.
Dec.	31	Reinstatement of Reid's account.
	31	Collection of cash from Reid.

General Journal

DATE	ACCOUNT TITLES AND EXPLANATIONS	POST REF.	DEBIT	CREDIT

Starter 9–9 ④

Northern Consultants accepts MasterCard credit cards from its customers. Assume Northern makes a sale of $2,000 and the credit card company charges a 3 percent fee. Provide the journal entry on June 22 to record the sales revenue.

<table>
<tr><td colspan="6" align="center">**General Journal**</td></tr>
<tr><td colspan="2">DATE</td><td>ACCOUNT TITLES AND EXPLANATIONS</td><td>POST REF.</td><td>DEBIT</td><td>CREDIT</td></tr>
<tr><td></td><td></td><td></td><td></td><td></td><td></td></tr>
<tr><td></td><td></td><td></td><td></td><td></td><td></td></tr>
<tr><td></td><td></td><td></td><td></td><td></td><td></td></tr>
<tr><td></td><td></td><td></td><td></td><td></td><td></td></tr>
<tr><td></td><td></td><td></td><td></td><td></td><td></td></tr>
<tr><td></td><td></td><td></td><td></td><td></td><td></td></tr>
<tr><td></td><td></td><td></td><td></td><td></td><td></td></tr>
<tr><td></td><td></td><td></td><td></td><td></td><td></td></tr>
</table>

Starter 9–11 ⑤

For each of the following notes receivable, compute the amount of interest revenue earned during 2017. Use a 365-day year or base your calculations on the number of months, depending on how the interest period is stated, and round only your answer to the nearest dollar.

	Principal	Interest Rate	Interest Period During 2017
Note 1	$200,000	8%	6 months
Note 2	30,000	4	75 days
Note 3	20,000	9	60 days
Note 4	100,000	5	3 months

Starter 9–14 ⑥

Vision Electronics, which makes DVD players, reported the following items at February 28, 2017 (amounts in thousands, with last year's—2016—amounts also given as needed):

Accounts Payable	$1,796	Accounts Receivable, net:	
Cash	860	February 28, 2017	$ 440
Inventories:		February 29, 2016	300
February 28, 2017	380	Cost of Goods Sold	4,800
February 29, 2016	320	Short-term investments	330
Net sales revenue	7,720	Other current assets	180
Long-term assets	820	Other current liabilities	290
Long-term liabilities	20		

Compute for 2017 Vision Electronics' (a) acid-test ratio, (b) days' sales in average receivables, (c) current ratio, (d) debt ratio, (e) gross margin percent, (f) inventory turnover. Evaluate each ratio value as strong or weak. Assume Vision Electronics sells on terms of net 30.

a. Acid-test ratio

b. Days' sales in average receivables

c. Current ratio

d. Debt ratio

e. Gross margin percentage

f. Rate of inventory

Starter 9–16 ⑦

In determining how accounts should be presented, accountants are concerned about the values being both relevant and reliable. Is the accounts receivable value presented on the balance sheet both relevant and reliable under IFRS?

_____

Exercise 9–1 ①

From the following list of adjusted account balances, prepare the current asset section of Delainey's Hardscaping for December 31, 2017. Assume all accounts have normal balances.

Accounts receivable	$51,000	Inventory	$22,000
Bad debt expense	1,200	Cash	15,000
Notes receivable, due August 31, 2018	12,000	Accumulated Amortization, Equipment	5,000
Supplies	1,440	Allowance for doubtful accounts	3,500
Notes receivable, due August 31, 2020	5,300	Equipment	25,000

Exercise 9–3 ②

On February 28, Big White Ski Equipment had a $25,500 debit balance in Accounts Receivable. During March, the company had sales of $65,500, which included $60,000 in credit sales. March collections were $53,000, and write-offs of uncollectible receivables totalled $1,250. Other data include:

a. February 28 credit balance in Allowance for Doubtful Accounts is $1,300.

b. Bad debt expense is estimated as 3 percent of credit sales.

Required

1. Prepare journal entries to record sales, collections, write-offs of uncollectibles during March, and bad debt expense by the allowance method (using the percent-of-sales method). Use March 31 as the journal entry date. Explanations are not required.

2. Prepare T-accounts to show the ending balances in Accounts Receivable and Allowance for Doubtful Accounts. Compute *net* Accounts Receivable at March 31. How much does Big White expect to collect?

Requirement 1

General Journal

DATE	ACCOUNT TITLES AND EXPLANATIONS	POST REF.	DEBIT	CREDIT

Requirement 2

Accounts Receivable	Allowance for Doubtful Accounts

Exercise 9–4 ②

Lui Dental began operations in January 2017 selling dental appliances to dentists. The following transactions occurred during the first six months of operations:

Jan.   15   Sold appliances to Dr. Hall on account for $15,750; cost $6,400.

Feb.   22   Received payment in full from Dr. Hall.

Mar.   4   Sold merchandise to Dr. Evans on account for $4,400; cost $1,250.

Apr.   20   Sold merchandise to Dr. Murray on account for $6,700; cost $2,990.

May   31   Sold merchandise to Dr. Kim on account for $3,200; cost $1,100.

Jun.   28   Received $3,000 on account from Dr. Evans.

Required

1. Complete the following aged listing of customer accounts as of June 30, 2017:

	Age of Account				
Customer	1–30 days	31–60 days	61–90 days	Over 90 days	Total
Dr. Evans					
Dr. Hall					
Dr. Kim	3,200				3,200
Dr. Murray					

2. Estimate the Allowance for Doubtful Accounts required at June 30, 2017, assuming the following uncollectible rates: 30 days, 2 percent; 60 days, 5 percent; 90 days, 15 percent; >90 days, 50 percent.

3. Show how Lui Dental would report its accounts receivable on its June 30, 2017, balance sheet. What amounts would be reported on an income statement prepared for the six-month period ended June 30, 2017?

4. If Dr. Evans's account needed to be written off in September 2017, how accurate is Lui Dental at estimating its bad debts?

Requirement 1

Customer	Age of Account				
	1–30 days	31–60 days	61–90 days	Over 90 days	Total

Requirement 2

Requirement 3

Requirement 4

Exercise 9–11 ④

Record the following transactions in the general journal of Jesse's Quick Clean Service. Assume Scotiabank charges merchants $0.50 per debit card transaction and MasterCard charges 4 percent of sales as service fees.

Mar. 31 Scotiabank debit card sales of $22,000, consisting of 1,500 transactions.

31 MasterCard credit card sales of $33,000.

Mar. 31 FleetPlan card accepted for $2,800 of payments. This card requires that receipts are submitted for payment manually. A 2 percent fee applies.

April 10 Payment was received from FleetPlan.

	General Journal			
DATE	ACCOUNT TITLES AND EXPLANATIONS	POST REF.	DEBIT	CREDIT

Exercise 9–12 ⑥

Franklin Ltd., a gift store, reported the following amounts in its 2017 financial statements. The 2016 figures are given for comparison.

		2017			2016
Current assets:					
Cash		$ 12,000			$ 26,000
Short-term investments		46,000			22,000
Accounts receivable	$120,000			$148,000	
Less: Allow. for uncollectibles	20,000	100,000		18,000	130,000
Inventory		384,000			378,000
Prepaid insurance		4,000			4,000
Total current assets		$ 546,000			$ 560,000
Total current liabilities		$ 218,000			$ 224,000
Net sales		$1,460,000			$1,464,000

Required

1. Determine whether Franklin Ltd.'s acid-test ratio improved or deteriorated from 2016 to 2017. How does Franklin Ltd.'s acid-test ratio compare with the industry average of 0.90?

2. Compare the days' sales in receivables measure for 2017 with the company's credit terms of net 30. What action, if any, should Franklin Ltd. take?

3. Indicate the most likely effect of the following changes in credit policy on the days' sales in receivables (+ for increase, – for decrease, and NE for no effect):

   a. Granted credit to people with poor credit history.

   b. Increased collection techniques or methods.

   c. Granted credit with discounts for early payment.

Requirements 1 & 2

_____

_____

_____

_____

_____

_____

_____

_____

_____

_____

_____

_____

_____

Requirements 1 & 2 (Continued)

_____

_____

_____

_____

_____

_____

_____

_____

_____

_____

_____

_____

_____

_____

_____

_____

_____

_____

_____

_____

_____

_____

Calculations:

Requirement 3

a. _____

b. _____

c. _____

Exercise 9–13 ⑤

Tropical North Company, which has a December 31 year end and uses a periodic inventory system, completed the following transactions during 2016 and 2017:

2016

Oct.	14	Sold merchandise to OFTR Racing, receiving a 60-day, 6 percent note for $5,000.
Nov.	16	Sold merchandise to Sunshine Racing receiving a 72-day, 4 percent note for $7,500.
Dec.	13	Received amount due from OFTR Racing.
Dec.	31	Accrued interest on the Sunshine Racing note.

2017

Jan.	27	Collected in full from Sunshine Company.

Required Prepare the necessary journal entries to record the above transactions. Assume that a 365-day year is used for calculations.

General Journal

DATE	ACCOUNT TITLES AND EXPLANATIONS	POST REF.	DEBIT	CREDIT

Exercise 9–18   ②

Lee Management Consulting wants to follow generally accepted accounting principles and use the allowance method for receivables. Michael Lee, owner of Lee Management Consulting, has decided that the best way to estimate uncollectibles would be to calculate 3.5 percent of credit sales. He has operated for several months and has not done this yet.

On November 10, 2016, Michael reviewed the list of outstanding accounts. He has identified that Gene is not going to pay his $900 receivable from July 19.

On November 16, 2016, Michael offered another client, Jin Lo, the opportunity to turn the unpaid account into a $1,000 note receivable. The note would incur 6 percent interest and be paid in three months.

Required

1. Journalize the entry on November 1, 2016, to record and establish the allowance for doubtful accounts using the percent-of-sales method for prior months' credit sales, which totalled $45,000.

2. Journalize the entry to record Gene's bad debt.

3. Journalize the establishment of the note receivable.

4. Prepare the journal entry that will be recorded on the date the note is settled (assuming it is settled on the maturity date).

Requirements 1 – 4

		General Journal			
DATE		ACCOUNT TITLES AND EXPLANATIONS	POST REF.	DEBIT	CREDIT

Requirements 1 – 4 (Continued)

DATE		**ACCOUNT TITLES AND EXPLANATIONS**	**POST REF.**	**DEBIT**	**CREDIT**

General Journal

Problem 9–2A ②

Matiere Co. completed the following transactions during 2016 and 2017:

2016

Dec. 31 Estimated that bad debt expense for the year was 3 percent of credit sales of $385,000 and recorded that amount as expense.

  31 Made the closing entry for bad debt expense.

2017

Mar. 26 Sold inventory to Mabel Sanders, $10,037.50, on credit terms of 2/10, n/30. Ignore cost of goods sold.

Sep. 15 Wrote off Mabel Sanders's account as uncollectible after repeated efforts to collect from her.

Nov. 10 Received $5,500 from Sanders, along with a letter stating her intention to pay her debt in full within 30 days. Reinstated her account in full.

Dec. 5 Received the balance due from Sanders.

  31 Made a compound entry to write off the following accounts as uncollectible: Curt Major, $2,200; Bernadette Lalonde, $962.50; Ellen Smart, $1,470.

  31 Estimated that bad debt expense for the year was 2 percent of credit sales of $490,000 and recorded the expense.

  31 Made the closing entry for bad debt expense.

Required

1. Open three-column general ledger accounts for Allowance for Doubtful Accounts and Bad Debt Expense. Keep running balances.

2. Record the transactions in the general journal and post to the ledger accounts.

3. The December 31, 2017, balance of Accounts Receivable is $146,000. Show how Accounts Receivable would be reported at that date.

4. Assume that Matiere Co. begins aging accounts receivable on December 31, 2017. The balance in Accounts Receivable is $146,000, the credit balance in Allowance for Doubtful Accounts is $16,717.50 (use your calculations from Requirement 3), and the company estimates that $19,900 of its accounts receivable will prove uncollectible.

   a. Make the adjusting entry for uncollectibles.

   b. Show how Accounts Receivable will be reported on the December 31, 2017, balance sheet after this adjusting entry.

Requirement 1

ACCOUNT: ALLOWANCE FOR DOUBTFUL ACCOUNTS

DATE		ITEM	JRNL. REF	DEBIT	CREDIT	BALANCE

ACCOUNT: BAD DEBT EXPENSE

DATE		ITEM	JRNL. REF.	DEBIT	CREDIT	BALANCE

Requirement 2

General Journal

DATE		ACCOUNT TITLES AND EXPLANATIONS	POST REF.	DEBIT	CREDIT

Requirement 3

Requirement 4a

General Journal

DATE	ACCOUNT TITLES AND EXPLANATIONS	POST REF.	DEBIT	CREDIT

Requirement 4b

Problem 9–6A ④ ⑤

Record the following selected transactions in the general journal of WM Gaming Supplies. Explanations are not required.

2016

Nov. 21 Received an $18,000, 60-day, 4 percent note from Barb Nuefield on account.

30 Recorded VISA credit card sales of $26,000. VISA charges 3 percent of sales.

Dec. 31 Made an adjusting entry to accrue interest on the Nuefield note.

31 Made an adjusting entry to record bad debt expense based on 3 percent of credit sales of $1,950,000.

31 Made a compound closing entry for Interest Revenue and Bad Debt Expense (ignore credit card sales and charges).

2017

Jan. 20 Collected the maturity value of the Nuefield note.

Mar. 14 Lent $20,000 cash to Morgan Supplies, receiving a six-month, 5 percent note.

30 Received a $5,600, 30-day, 10 percent note from Quin Carson on his past-due account receivable.

May 29 Carson dishonoured (failed to pay) his note at maturity; after attempting to collect his note for one month, wrote off the account as uncollectible.

Sep. 14 Collected the maturity value of the Morgan Supplies note.

30 Wrote off as uncollectible the accounts receivable of Sue Parsons, $3,250 and Mac Gally, $5,200.

General Journal

DATE	ACCOUNT TITLES AND EXPLANATIONS	POST REF.	DEBIT	CREDIT

General Journal

DATE		ACCOUNT TITLES AND EXPLANATIONS	POST REF.	DEBIT	CREDIT

Problem 9–9A ⑥

The comparative financial statements of Sopa Company for 2017, 2016, and 2015 included the following selected data:

	2017	2016	2015
	(in thousands)		
Balance Sheet			
Current assets:			
Cash	$ 80	$ 80	$ 40
Short-term investments	280	400	240
Receivables, net	760	600	480
Inventories	1,680	1,520	1,360
Prepaid expenses	120	120	80
Total current assets	$ 2,920	$ 2,720	$ 2,200
Total current liabilities	$ 1,920	$ 1,640	$ 1,520
Income Statement			
Sales revenue	$10,400	$10,000	$ 7,600

Required

1. Compute these ratios for 2017 and 2016:
   a. Current ratio
   b. Acid-test ratio
   c. Days' sales in receivables
2. Write a brief memo explaining to Tony Crane, owner of Sopa Company, which ratio values showed improvement from 2016 to 2017 and which ratio values deteriorated. Discuss whether this trend is favourable or unfavourable for the company.

Requirement 1

	2017	2016
A. CURRENT RATIO:		

B. ACID-TEST RATIO:

C. DAYS' SALES IN AVERAGE RECEIVABLES:

Requirement 2

_____
_____
_____
_____
_____
_____
_____
_____
_____
_____
_____
_____
_____
_____
_____
_____
_____
_____
_____
_____
_____
_____
_____

*Problem 9–10A Ⓐ①

A company received the following notes during 2017. The notes were discounted on the dates and at the rates indicated.

Note	Date	Principal Amount	Interest Rate	Term	Date Discounted	Discount Rate
(a)	Jun. 15	$20,000	8%	60 days	Jul. 15	12%
(b)	Aug. 1	9,000	10	90 days	Aug. 27	12
(c)	Nov. 21	12,000	15	90 days	Dec. 4	15

Required Identify each note by letter, compute interest using a 365-day year for all notes, round all interest amounts to the nearest cent, and present entries in general journal form. Explanations are not required.

1. Determine the due date and maturity value of each note.
2. Determine the discount and proceeds from the sale (discounting) of each note.
3. Journalize the discounting of notes (a) and (b).

Requirement 1

NOTE	DUE DATE	PRINCIPAL + INTEREST		MATURITY VALUE
(a)	_____	_____	=	_____
(b)	_____	_____	=	_____
(c)	_____	_____	=	_____

Requirement 2

NOTE	MATURITY VALUE		DISCOUNT		PROCEEDS
(a)	_____	−	_____	=	_____
(b)	_____	−	_____	=	_____
(c)	_____	−	_____	=	_____

Requirement 3

General Journal					
DATE		ACCOUNT TITLES AND EXPLANATIONS	POST REF.	DEBIT	CREDIT

10 PROPERTY, PLANT, AND EQUIPMENT; AND GOODWILL AND INTANGIBLE ASSETS

LEARNING OBJECTIVES

1 Measure the cost of property, plant, and equipment.
2 Calculate and account for amortization.
3 Account for other issues: Amortization for income tax purposes, partial years, and revised assumptions.
4 Account for the disposal of property, plant, and equipment.
5 Account for natural resources.
6 Account for intangible assets and goodwill.
7 Describe the impact of IFRS on property, plant, and equipment, intangible assets, and goodwill.

Starter 10–6 ②

At the beginning of 2017, FlyFast Airways purchased a used Boeing jet at a cost of $50,000,000. FlyFast expects the plane to remain useful for five years (6,000,000 miles) and to have a residual value of $4,000,000. FlyFast expects the plane to be flown 750,000 miles the first year. (Note: "Miles" is the unit of measure used in the airline industry.)

1. Compute FlyFast's first-year amortization on the jet using the following methods:
   a. Straight line   b. UOP   c. DDB
2. Show the jet's book value at the end of the first year under the straight-line method.

Requirements 1 & 2

Starter 10–8 ③

This exercise uses the FlyFast Airways data from Starter 10-6. FlyFast is comparing the CCA method used for income tax purposes with the straight-line amortization method.

1. Calculate the amount of CCA, at a rate of 25 percent, that FlyFast will be able to claim in its first year.
2. Why does the Government of Canada, through the CCA, regulate the amount of amortization that a company can claim for income tax purposes?

Requirements 1 & 2

_____
_____
_____
_____
_____
_____
_____
_____
_____
_____
_____

Starter 10–11 ③

Red Pine Printers purchased equipment on January 1, 2013, for $250,000. The estimated residual value is $25,000 and the estimated useful life is 15 years. Red Pine Printers uses the straight-line method for amortization of its equipment. On January 1, 2016, Red Pine Printers revised the useful life to be nine more years rather than 12. How much amortization would be recorded on December 31, 2016?

_____
_____
_____
_____

Starter 10–12 ③

A fully amortized asset has a cost of $100,000 and zero residual value.

1. What is the asset's accumulated amortization? What is its carrying value?
2. The asset cost $100,000. Now suppose its residual value is $10,000. How much is its accumulated amortization if it is fully amortized?

_____
_____
_____
_____

Starter 10–14 ④

In 2015, Global Millwrights purchased a milling machine for $4,000, debiting Milling Equipment. During 2015 and 2016, Global recorded total amortization of $2,000 on the machine. In January 2017, Global traded in the machine for a new one with a fair market value of $4,200, paying $2,700 cash. This exchange transaction has commercial substance. Journalize Global Millwrights' exchange of machines on January 15.

General Journal				
DATE	ACCOUNT TITLES AND EXPLANATIONS	POST REF.	DEBIT	CREDIT

Exercise 10–2 ①

India Trucking bought three used trucks for $60,000. An independent appraisal of the trucks produced the following figures:

Truck No.	Appraised Value
1	$24,000
2	22,000
3	20,000

India Trucking paid $21,000 in cash and signed a note for the remainder. Record the purchase in the general journal on February 1 identifying each truck's individual cost in a separate Truck account.

General Journal					
DATE		ACCOUNT TITLES AND EXPLANATIONS	POST REF.	DEBIT	CREDIT

Exercise 10–3 ①

Classify each of the following expenditures related to the cost of a machine:

	Cost or Betterment	Repair or Expense	Other
a. Purchase price			
b. Provincial sales tax paid on the purchase price			
c. Transportation and insurance while the machine is in transport from seller to buyer			
d. Installation			
e. Training of personnel for initial operation of the machine			
f. Special reinforcement to the machine platform			
g. Income tax paid on income earned from the sale of products manufactured by the machine			
h. Major overhaul to extend the machine's useful life by three years			
i. Ordinary recurring repairs to keep the machine in good working order			
j. Lubrication before the machine is placed in service			
k. Periodic lubrication after the machine is placed in service			
l. GST on the purchase price			

Exercise 10–5 ②

On January 1, 2017, Murray Demolition, a Hamilton, Ontario, company specializing in blasting and removing buildings, purchased and took delivery of a new dump truck to add to its growing fleet. Murray Demolition has a high-class reputation and uses only the best and newest equipment on their worksites. The business spent $140,000 plus HST on the truck, which is expected to be useful to the business for four years, at which time it should be able to be sold for $60,000. Murray Demolition has always used the straight-line basis of calculating amortization. The new owners want to see the amortization schedules for the straight-line, UOP, and DDB methods just to be sure this makes sense. The business expects the truck to be useful for 200,000 kilometres—60,000 kilometres in Year 1; 50,000 kilometres in each of Years 2 and 3; and 40,000 kilometres in Year 4.

Straight-Line Amortization Schedule

DATE	ASSET COST	AMORTIZATION RATE	×	AMORTIZATION COST	=	Amortization for the Year AMORTIZATION EXPENSE	ACCUMULATED AMORTIZATION	ASSET BOOK VALUE

Units-of-Production Amortization Schedule

DATE	ASSET COST	AMORTIZATION PER ___	×	NUMBER OF ___	=	Amortization for the Year AMORTIZATION EXPENSE	ACCUMULATED AMORTIZATION	ASSET BOOK VALUE

Double-Declining-Balance Amortization Schedule

DATE	ASSET COST	DDB RATE	×	AMORTIZATION COST	=	AMORTIZATION EXPENSE	ACCUMULATED AMORTIZATION	ASSET BOOK VALUE
				Amortization for the Year				

Calculations:

Exercise 10–10 ② ④

On January 13, 2016, Yeung's Gifts purchased store fixtures for $65,000 cash, expecting the fixtures to remain in service for 10 years. Yeung's Gifts has amortized the fixtures on a DDB basis with an estimated residual value of $5,000. On September 30, 2017, Yeung's Gifts sold the fixtures for $19,150 cash because they were not "green" technology. Record the amortization expense on the fixtures for the years ended December 31, 2016, and 2017, and the sale of the fixtures on September 30, 2017. Round all calculations to the nearest dollar.

General Journal

DATE		ACCOUNT TITLES AND EXPLANATIONS	POST REF.	DEBIT	CREDIT

Calculations:

Exercise 10–12 ① ② ④

Triad Freight is a large warehousing and distribution company that operates throughout Eastern Canada. Triad Freight uses the UOP method to amortize its trucks because its managers believe UOP amortization best measures the wear and tear on the trucks. Triad Freight trades in used trucks often to keep driver morale high and to maximize fuel efficiency. Consider these facts about one Mack truck in the company's fleet:

When acquired in 2013, the tractor/trailer rig cost $585,000 and was expected to remain in service for eight years, or 1,500,000 kilometres. Estimated residual value was $60,000. The truck was driven 150,000 kilometres in 2014, 195,000 kilometres in 2015, and 235,000 kilometres in 2016. After 100,000 kilometres in 2017, the company traded in the Mack truck for a Freightliner rig with a fair market value of $510,000 on August 15. Triad Freight paid cash of $40,000. This trade-in will bring in significantly more income to Triad Freight by reducing operating costs. Determine Triad Freight's cost of the new truck. Prepare the journal entry to record the trade-in.

Calculations

General Journal

DATE	ACCOUNT TITLES AND EXPLANATIONS	POST REF.	DEBIT	CREDIT

Exercise 10–14 ③ ⑥

Biikman Company manufactures flat-screen monitors for the graphics industry and has recently purchased for $525,000 a patent for the design of a new monitor. Although it gives legal protection for 20 years, the patent is expected to provide Biikman Company with a competitive advantage for only 10 years. After using the patent for two years, Biikman Company learns at an industry trade show that Ir Company is designing a more effective monitor. Based on this new information, Biikman Company decides to amortize the remaining cost of the patent over the current year, giving the patent a total useful life of three years.

Required

1. Prepare the journal entry to record the purchase of the patent.
2. Assume straight-line amortization is used. Record the journal entry for amortization in Year 1.
3. Record amortization for Year 3.

Requirements 1 – 3

		General Journal			
DATE		ACCOUNT TITLES AND EXPLANATIONS	POST REF.	DEBIT	CREDIT

Calculations:

Exercise 10–19 ⑦

Note 1 of the notes to the financial statements (page 58) of the Loblaw 2013 Annual Report reads as follows:

> For the purpose of impairment testing, assets are grouped together into the smallest group of assets that generate cash inflows from continuing use that are largely independent of cash inflows of other assets or groups of assets. This grouping is referred to as a cash generating unit ("CGU"). The Company has determined that each location is a separate CGU for purposes of impairment testing.

Required

1. What is the "cash generating unit" for Loblaw?
2. How is this different from when the company followed the previous Canadian GAAP rules, which were similar to those described in this chapter?

Requirements 1 & 2

_____

_____

_____

_____

_____

_____

_____

_____

_____

_____

_____

_____

_____

Exercise 10–20 ②

In Chapter 2, on page 98, we learned that Lee Management Consulting had paid $1,000 cash for a Dell computer on June 3, 2016. The computer is expected to be useful for four years. On June 4, 2016, Lee Management Consulting purchased office furniture on account for $5,000. The furniture was expected to last for five years. Looking back through his records, Michael Lee sees that he recorded $42 of amortization for the equipment and $167 of amortization for the furniture in June. Both assets are assumed to have no residual value at the end of their useful life. Lee is not sure how this was calculated, so he needs some help figuring out the entry required for July 31, 2016.

Required

1. Calculate the amount of amortization for each asset for the month ended July 31, 2016, under the straight-line and double-declining-balance methods in order to figure out what method is being used for the journal entries. Round only the total amounts to the nearest dollar.
2. Which method results in the highest expense?
3. Is the method that results in the highest expense used? What reason would Michael Lee use to justify the choice of method?
4. Journalize the entry to record the amortization expense to July 31, 2016, using the double-declining-balance method results. Use a compound entry.
5. If in December it was learned that the furniture's estimated useful life is really not correct and it should actually last an additional six years from now, what would the December 31, 2016, journal entry look like? Assume all amortization was recorded up to November 30. Round only the journal entry to the nearest dollar.

Requirements 1 – 3

Requirement 4

General Journal

DATE	ACCOUNT TITLES AND EXPLANATIONS	POST REF.	DEBIT	CREDIT

Requirement 5

General Journal

DATE	ACCOUNT TITLES AND EXPLANATIONS	POST REF.	DEBIT	CREDIT

Problem 10–2A ②

On January 5, 2017, Paige Construction purchased a used crane at a total cost of $200,000. Before placing the crane in service, Paige spent $12,500 transporting it, $4,800 replacing parts, and $11,400 overhauling the engine. Karen Paige, the owner, estimates that the crane will remain in service for four years and have a residual value of $42,000. The crane's annual usage is expected to be 2,400 hours in each of the first three years and 2,200 hours in the fourth year. In trying to decide which amortization method to use, Mary Blundon, the accountant, requests an amortization schedule for each of the following generally accepted amortization methods: straight line, UOP, and DDB.

Required

1. Assuming Paige Construction amortizes this crane individually, prepare an amortization schedule for each of the three amortization methods listed, showing asset cost, amortization expense, accumulated amortization, and asset book value. Assume a December 31 year end.

2. Paige Construction prepares financial statements for its bankers using the amortization method that maximizes reported income in the early years of asset use. Identify the amortization method that meets the company's objective.

Calculations:

Requirement 1

Straight-Line Amortization Schedule

Amortization for the Year

DATE	ASSET COST	AMORTIZATION RATE	×	AMORTIZATION COST	=	AMORTIZATION EXPENSE	ACCUMULATED AMORTIZATION	ASSET BOOK VALUE

Units-of-Production Amortization Schedule

Amortization for the Year

DATE	ASSET COST	AMORTIZATION PER ___	×	NUMBER OF ___	=	AMORTIZATION EXPENSE	ACCUMULATED AMORTIZATION	ASSET BOOK VALUE

Requirement 1 (Continued)

Double-Declining-Balance Amortization Schedule

DATE	ASSET COST	DDB RATE	AMORTIZATION COST	AMORTIZATION EXPENSE	ACCUMULATED AMORTIZATION	ASSET BOOK VALUE
		×	Amortization for the Year	=		

Requirement 2

Calculations:

Problem 10–3A ① ② ③

Stefano Distributors incurred the following costs in acquiring land and a building, making land improvements, and constructing and furnishing an office building for its own use:

a.	Purchase price of 2 hectares of land, including an old building that will be used for storage of maintenance equipment (land appraised market value is $1,300,000; building appraised market value is $300,000)	$1,150,000
b.	Real estate taxes in arrears on the land to be paid by Stefano Distributors	6,000
c.	Additional dirt and earth moving	6,000
d.	Legal fees on the land acquisition	4,500
e.	Fence around the boundary of the land	70,000
f.	Building permit for the office building	1,000
g.	Architect fee for the design of the office building	40,000
h.	Company signs near front and rear approaches to the company property	14,000
i.	Renovation of the storage building	150,000
j.	Concrete, wood, steel girders, and other materials used in the construction of the office building	700,000
k.	Masonry, carpentry, roofing, and other labour to construct the office building	550,000
l.	Parking lots and concrete walks on the property	31,500
m.	Lights for the parking lot, walkways, and company signs	12,500
n.	Salary of construction supervisor (90 percent to office building and 10 percent to storage building)	100,000
o.	Office furniture for the office building	125,000
p.	Transportation of furniture from seller to the office building	2,000

Stefano Distributors amortizes buildings over 40 years, land improvements over 20 years, and furniture over 6 years, all on a straight-line basis with zero residual value.

Required

1. Set up columns for Land, Land Improvements, Office Building, Storage Building, and Furniture. Show how to account for each of Stefano's costs by listing the cost under the correct account. Determine the total cost of each asset.

2. Assuming that all construction was complete and the assets were placed in service on February 25, record amortization for the year ended December 31. Round figures to the nearest dollar.

Requirement 1

ITEM	LAND	LAND IMPROVEMENTS	OFFICE BUILDING	STORAGE BUILDING	FURNITURE

Calculations:

Requirement 2

General Journal

DATE		ACCOUNT TITLES AND EXPLANATIONS	POST REF.	DEBIT	CREDIT

Calculations:

Problem 10–5A ① ② ③ ④

Assume that Rees Warehousing completed the following transactions:

2016

Mar. 3   Paid $8,000 cash for a used forklift.

5   Paid $1,500 to have the forklift engine overhauled.

7   Paid $1,000 to have the forklift modified for specialized moving of large flat-screen televisions.

Nov. 3   Paid $550 for an oil change and regular maintenance.

Dec. 31   Used the DDB method to record amortization on the forklift. (Assume a three-year life and no residual value.)

2017

Feb. 13   Replaced the forklift's broken fork for $400 cash, the deductible on Rees Warehousing's insurance. The new fork will not increase the useful life of the forklift.

Jul. 10   Traded in the forklift for a new forklift costing $18,000. The dealer granted a $3,000 allowance on the old forklift, and Rees Warehousing paid the balance in cash. Recorded 2017 amortization for the year to date and then recorded the exchange of forklifts. This transaction has commercial substance.

Dec. 31   Used the DDB method to record amortization on the new forklift. (Assume a five-year life and no residual value.)

Rees Warehousing's amortization policy indicates that the company will take a full month's amortization on purchases occurring up to and on the 15th day of the month and will not take any amortization for the month if the transaction occurs after the 15th day of the month.

Required Record the transactions in the general journal, indicating whether each transaction amount should be capitalized as an asset or expensed. Round all calculations to the nearest dollar.

DATE		ACCOUNT TITLES AND EXPLANATIONS	POST REF.	DEBIT	CREDIT
General Journal					

General Journal

DATE		ACCOUNT TITLES AND EXPLANATIONS	POST REF.	DEBIT	CREDIT

Calculations:

Problem 10–7A ⑤

Oilco Canada Limited sells refined petroleum products. The company's balance sheet includes reserves of oil assets.

Suppose Oilco paid $15 million cash for an oil lease that contained an estimated reserve of 1,990,000 barrels of oil. Assume that the company paid $550,000 for additional geological tests of the property and $170,000 to prepare the surface for drilling. Prior to production, the company signed a $120,000 note payable to have a building constructed on the property. Because the building provides onsite headquarters for the drilling effort and will be abandoned when the oil is depleted, its cost is debited to the Oil Properties account and included in amortization charges. During the first year of production, Oilco removed 125,000 barrels of oil, which it sold on credit for $75 per barrel.

Required

1. Make general journal entries to record all transactions related to the oil and gas property, including amortization and sale of the first-year production. Dates are not required.

2. Show the accounts and amounts that would be presented on the balance sheet.

Requirement 1

General Journal

DATE	ACCOUNT TITLES AND EXPLANATIONS	POST REF.	DEBIT	CREDIT

Requirement 1 (Continued)

General Journal

DATE		ACCOUNT TITLES AND EXPLANATIONS	POST REF.	DEBIT	CREDIT

Calculations:

Requirement 2

Problem 10–8A ⑥

Part 1 CTS Canada provides telephone service to most of Canada. Assume that CTS Canada purchased another company that had the following totals on its financial statements:

Book value of assets..	$1,536,000
Market value of assets...	1,800,000
Liabilities...	540,000

Required

1. Make the general journal entry to record CTS Canada's purchase of the other company for $1,620,000 cash on April 3.

2. How should CTS Canada account for goodwill at year end and in the future? Explain in detail.

Part 2 Suppose BlackBerry Ltd. purchased a patent for $1,400,000 on January 1. Before using the patent, BlackBerry incurred an additional cost of $250,000 for a lawsuit to defend the company's right to purchase it. Even though the patent gives BlackBerry legal protection for 20 years, company management has decided to amortize its cost over an 8-year period because of the industry's fast-changing technologies.

Required

1. Make general journal entries to record the patent transactions, including straight-line amortization for one year at December 31.

2. Show the accounts and amounts that would be presented on the balance sheet.

Part 1

Requirement 1

		General Journal			
DATE		ACCOUNT TITLES AND EXPLANATIONS	POST REF.	DEBIT	CREDIT

Requirement 2

Part 2

Requirement 1

	General Journal			
DATE	ACCOUNT TITLES AND EXPLANATIONS	POST REF.	DEBIT	CREDIT

Requirement 2

11 CURRENT LIABILITIES AND PAYROLL

LEARNING OBJECTIVES

1 Account for current liabilities of a known amount.
2 Account for current liabilities that must be estimated.
3 Compute payroll amounts.
4 Record basic payroll transactions.
5 Report payroll and other current liabilities on the balance sheet.
6 Describe the impact of IFRS on current liabilities.

Starter 11-5 ①

On July 10, Keller Company, a business located in Alberta, purchased $15,000 of inventory for resale on account. On July 25, Keller recorded the sale of that merchandise on account for $20,000 plus tax. On August 10, Keller remitted GST to the Receiver General. They had no other sales or input tax credits. Journalize all three transactions.

General Journal

DATE	ACCOUNT TITLES AND EXPLANATIONS	POST REF.	DEBIT	CREDIT

Starter 11-7 ①

On December 31, 2016, Jabot purchased $16,000 of equipment on a one-year, 9 percent note payable. Journalize the company's purchase of equipment, the accrual of interest expense on May 31, 2017 (its fiscal year end), and the payment of the note plus interest on December 31, 2017.

General Journal

DATE	ACCOUNT TITLES AND EXPLANATIONS	POST REF.	DEBIT	CREDIT

General Journal

DATE		ACCOUNT TITLES AND EXPLANATIONS	POST REF.	DEBIT	CREDIT

Starter 11-8 ②

Western Yard Equipment offers warranties on all its lawn mowers. It estimates warranty expense at 1.4 percent of sales. At the beginning of 2016, the Estimated Warranty Payable account had a credit balance of $2,200. During the year, Western Yard Equipment had $580,000 of sales and had to pay out $8,950 in warranty payments for repairs.

1. Prepare the required journal entries to record warranty expense and payments. Use December 31 for the journal entry date.
2. What is the balance of the warranty liability at the end of 2016? Indicate whether the balance is a debit or a credit.

Requirement 1

General Journal

DATE		ACCOUNT TITLES AND EXPLANATIONS	POST REF.	DEBIT	CREDIT

Requirement 2

Warranty Payable

Exercise 11-1 ①

Prepare the journal entries for Passport Merchandising, assuming that Passport Merchandising uses a perpetual inventory system. Passport Merchandising charges GST on all its sales at the rate of 5 percent and pays GST on all its purchases at the rate of 5 percent. Explanations are not required.

May	8	Purchased inventory, on account, FOB destination, from Seguin Wholesale. $2,000 plus applicable GST.
	10	Returned defective merchandise to Seguin, $300 plus applicable GST.
	12	Sold merchandise to Dainty Store on account for $3,000 plus applicable GST. Cost of the merchandise sold was $1,300.
	28	Collected balance on account from Dainty Store.
	30	Paid balance on account to Seguin.
June	15	Prepare the remittance payment of GST based on only the above transactions in May.

General Journal

DATE		ACCOUNT TITLES AND EXPLANATIONS	POST REF.	DEBIT	CREDIT

Exercise 11-3 ①

Make general journal entries to record the following transactions of Mehta Products for a two-month period:

Jun. 30   Recorded cash sales of $115,000 for the month plus PST of 8 percent collected on behalf of the province of Manitoba and GST of 5 percent. Record the two taxes in separate accounts.

Jul. 6   Sent June PST and GST to the appropriate authorities (Minister of Finance for PST and Receiver General for GST). Assume no GST input tax credits.

General Journal

DATE	ACCOUNT TITLES AND EXPLANATIONS	POST REF.	DEBIT	CREDIT

Exercise 11-4 ①

Suppose Detweiler Technologies borrowed $2,000,000 on December 31, 2013, by issuing 4 percent long-term debt that must be paid in four equal annual instalments plus interest commencing January 2, 2015.

Required   Insert the appropriate amounts in the following excerpts from the company's partial balance sheet to show how Detweiler Technologies should report its current and long-term liabilities for this debt.

	December 31,			
	2014	**2015**	**2016**	**2017**
Current liabilities:				
Current portion of long-term debt	$ _____	$ _____	$ _____	$ _____
Interest payable	$ _____	$ _____	$ _____	$ _____
Long-term liabilities:				
Long-term debt	$ _____	$ _____	$ _____	$ _____

Calculations:

Exercise 11-12 ③

Sylvia Chan is a clerk in the shoe department of the Hudson's Bay store in Winnipeg. She earns a base monthly salary of $1,875 plus a 7 percent commission on her sales. Through payroll deductions, Chan donates $50 per month to a charitable organization and pays benefit premiums of $49.15. Compute Chan's gross pay and net pay for December, assuming her sales for the month are $50,000. The income tax rate on her earnings is 20 percent, the CPP contribution rate is 4.95 percent (account for the $3,500 basic annual exemption), and the EI premium rate is 1.88 percent. Chan has not yet reached the CPP or EI maximum earning levels.

Exercise 11-13 ③ ④

Brad Jackson works for a Bob's Burgers takeout for straight-time earnings of $10.50 per hour with time and a half for hours in excess of 35 per week. Jackson's payroll deductions include income tax of 25 percent, CPP of 4.95 percent on earnings (account for the $3,500 basic annual exemption), and EI of 1.88 percent on earnings. In addition, he contributes $10 per week to his Registered Retirement Savings Plan (RRSP). Assume Jackson worked 40 hours during the week. He has not yet reached the CPP or EI maximum earning levels.

Required

1. Compute Jackson's gross pay and net pay for the week.

2. Make a June 14 general journal entry to record the restaurant's wage expense for Jackson's work, including his payroll deductions and the employer payroll costs. Round all amounts to the nearest cent. An explanation is not required.

Requirement 1

Requirement 2

General Journal				
DATE	ACCOUNT TITLES AND EXPLANATIONS	POST REF.	DEBIT	CREDIT

Exercise 11-14 ③ ④

Natural Step Manufacturing incurred salary expense of $95,000 for September. The company's payroll expense includes CPP of 4.95 percent and EI of 1.4 times the employee payment, which is 1.88 percent of earnings. Also, the company provides the following benefits for employees: dental insurance (cost to the company of $5,723.09), life insurance (cost to the company of $441.09), and pension benefits through a private plan (cost to the company of $1,745.60). Record Natural Step Manufacturing's payroll expenses for CPP, EI, and employee benefits on September 30. Ignore the CPP basic exemption.

EXHIBIT 11–10 | Employee Earnings Record for 2014

Employee Name and Address:
Jenkins, Jason C.
XX Camousen Crescent
Victoria, BC

Social Insurance No.: 111 111 111
Marital Status: Married
Net Claims Code: 4
Pay Rate: $700 per week; overtime $26.25 per hour
Job Title: Admin. Assistant

Week Ended	Hours	Gross Pay				Deductions						Net Pay	
		Straight Time	Overtime	Total	To Date	Federal Income Tax	Province of BC Income Tax	CPP	EI	United Way	Total	Amount	Cheque No.
Jan. 4	40	700.00		700.00	700.00	47.60	18.16	31.32	13.16	2.00	112.24	587.76	403
Dec. 3	40	700.00		700.00	35,437.50	47.60	18.16	31.32	13.16	2.00	112.24	587.76	1525
Dec. 10	40	700.00		700.00	36,137.50	47.60	18.16	31.32	13.16	2.00	112.24	587.80	1548
Dec. 17	44	700.00	105.00	805.00	36,942.50	62.28	25.27	36.52	15.13	2.00	141.20	663.80	1574
Dec. 24	48	700.00	210.00	910.00	37,852.50	81.48	32.99	41.71	17.11	2.00	175.29	734.71	1598
Dec. 31	46	700.00	157.50	857.50	38,710.00	70.47	29.13	39.11	16.12	2.00	156.83	700.67	1632
Total		36,400.00	2,310.00	38,710.00	38,710.00	2,798.16	1,082.28	1,742.88	727.80	104.00	6,455.12	32,254.88	

Exercise 11-15 ⑤

Study the Employee Earnings Record for Jason C. Jenkins in Exhibit 11–10. In addition to the amounts shown in the exhibit, the employer also paid all employee benefits plus (a) an amount equal to 5 percent of gross pay into Jenkins's pension retirement account, and (b) dental insurance for Jenkins at a cost of $35 per month and parking of $10 per month. Compute the employer's total payroll expense for employee Jason C. Jenkins during 2015. Carry all amounts to the nearest cent.

Exercise 11-16 ① ⑤

Assume Salem Electronics completed these selected transactions during December 2016:

1. Music For You Inc., a chain of music stores, ordered $105,000 worth of CD players. With its order, Music For You Inc. sent a cheque for $105,000. Salem Electronics will ship the goods on January 3, 2017.

2. The December payroll of $600,000 is subject to employee withheld income tax of 16 percent, CPP expenses of 4.95 percent for the employee and 4.95 percent for the employer, and EI deductions of 1.88 percent for the employee and 1.4 times the employee rate of 1.88 percent for the employer. On December 31, Salem Electronics pays employees but accrues all tax amounts. Employees have not reached CPP or EI maximums.

3. Sales of $30,000,000 are subject to estimated warranty cost of 1 percent. This was the first year the company provided a warranty, and no warranty claims have been recorded or paid.

4. On December 2, Salem Electronics signed a $50,000 note payable that requires annual payments of $10,000 plus 5 percent interest on the unpaid balance each December 2. Salem calculates interest on this note based on days, not months.

Required   Report these items on Salem Electronics' balance sheet at December 31, 2016.

Calculations:

Exercise 11-17 ③ ④

In Chapter 2, on page 99, we learned that Lee Management Consulting hired a part-time office manager to be paid $2,000 salary per month. She started work on Monday, June 25. The following additional payroll information is available for the June 29 pay date:

Federal income tax to be withheld	$138.55
Provincial income tax to be withheld	99.70
CPP	84.56
EI	37.60

Required

1. Compute the office manager's gross pay and net pay for the month.

2. Make one general journal entry to record Lee Management Consulting's salary expense for the office manager, including her payroll deductions and the employer payroll costs. Round all amounts to the nearest cent.

Requirement 1

Requirement 2

General Journal

DATE		ACCOUNT TITLES AND EXPLANATIONS	POST REF.	DEBIT	CREDIT

Problem 11-1A ① ②

The following selected transactions of Truestar Communications, a Manitoba company, occurred during 2016 and 2017. The company's year end is December 31.

2016

Jan. 3   Purchased a machine at a cost of $350,000 plus 5 percent GST, signing a 5 percent, 180-day note payable for that amount.

      29   Recorded the month's sales of $1,570,000 (excludes PST and GST), 80 percent on credit and 20 percent for cash. Sales amounts are subject to 8 percent PST and 5 percent GST.

Feb. 5   Paid January's PST and GST to the appropriate authorities.

      28   Borrowed $3,000,000 on a 3 percent note payable that calls for annual instalment payments of $300,000 principal plus interest.

Jul. 3   Paid the six-month, 5 percent note at maturity.

Nov. 30   Purchased inventory for $150,000 plus GST, signing a six-month, 5 percent note payable.

Dec. 31   Accrued warranty expense, which is estimated at 2 percent of annual sales of $8,000,000.

      31   Accrued interest on all outstanding notes payable. Make a separate interest accrual entry for each note payable.

2017

Feb. 28   Paid the first instalment and interest for one year on the long-term note payable.

May 31   Paid off the 5 percent note plus interest at maturity.

Required   Record the transactions in the company's general journal. Use days in any interest accrual calculations, not months. Round all amounts to the nearest whole dollar. Explanations are not required.

General Journal

DATE	ACCOUNT TITLES AND EXPLANATIONS	POST REF.	DEBIT	CREDIT

General Journal

DATE		ACCOUNT TITLES AND EXPLANATIONS	POST REF.	DEBIT	CREDIT

Problem 11-3A ③

Required

1. Determine missing amounts a, b, c, and d.
2. Prepare the general journal entry to record Westwood Golf Shop's payroll on August 31. Credit Payroll Payable for net pay. No explanation is required.

Requirement 1

SUPPLY MISSING PAYROLL AMOUNTS

Employee Earnings

Regular employee earnings	$19,947	Medical insurance	$ 541
Overtime pay	_____ a	Total deductions..........................	7,947
Total employee earnings................	_____ b	Net pay	17,595

Deductions and Net Pay

Accounts Debited

Withheld income tax	6,379	Salaries Expense..........................	_____ d
Canada Pension Plan...................	_____ c	Wages Expense............................	6,938
Employment Insurance.................	478	Sales Commission Expense................	1,681

Requirement 2

General Journal

DATE	ACCOUNT TITLES AND EXPLANATIONS	POST REF.	DEBIT	CREDIT

Problem 11-4A ③ ④

Assume that Raji Patel is a vice-president in Maple Capital's leasing operations. During 2015 she worked for the company all year at a $7,500 monthly salary. She also earned a year-end bonus equal to 10 percent of her salary.

Patel's federal income tax withheld during 2015 was $2,398 per month. Also, there was a one-time federal withholding tax of $4,512 on her bonus cheque. She paid $356.85 per month into the CPP until she had paid the maximum of $2,479.95. In addition, Patel paid $157.50 per month EI through her employer until the maximum of $930.60 had been reached. She had authorized Maple Capital to make the following payroll deductions: RRSP contribution of $55 per month and United Way donation of $37.50 per month.

Maple Capital incurred CPP expense equal to the amount deducted from Patel's pay and EI expense equal to 1.4 times the amount Patel paid. In addition, Maple Capital paid dental and drug insurance of $38 per month and pension benefits of 7 percent of her base salary.

Required

1. Compute Patel's gross pay, payroll deductions, and net pay for the full year 2015. Round all amounts to the nearest cent.
2. Compute Maple Capital's total 2015 payroll expense for Patel.
3. Prepare Maple Capital's general journal entries (explanations are not required) to record its expense for the following:
   a. Patel's total earnings for the year, her payroll deductions, and her net pay. Debit Salary Expense and Bonus Expense as appropriate for salary and bonus. Credit liability accounts for the payroll deductions and Cash for net pay.
   b. Employer payroll expenses for Patel. Credit the appropriate liability accounts.
   c. Benefits provided to Patel. Credit Health Insurance Payable and Company Pension Payable.

Requirement 1

Requirement 2

Requirement 3

General Journal

DATE	ACCOUNT TITLES AND EXPLANATIONS	POST REF.	DEBIT	CREDIT

Problem 11-5A ③ ④ ⑤

The payroll records of Radii Video Productions Inc. provide the following information for the weekly pay period ended September 21:

Employee	Hours Worked	Hourly Earnings Rate	Income Tax	Canada Pension Plan	Employment Insurance	United Way	Year-to-Date Earnings at End of Previous Week
Molly Dodge	43	$30	$474.10	$ 0	$ 0	$25	$51,500
Tally Allard	40	13	67.60	22.41	9.52	2	19,760
George White	49	10	63.70	23.15	9.79	2	20,250
Luigi Valenti	42	20	352.00	39.24	0	5	49,950

Tally Allard and George White work in the office, and Molly Dodge and Luigi Valenti work in sales. All employees are paid time and a half for hours worked in excess of 40 hours per week. Assume that the company contributes an amount equal to 8 percent of each employee's gross pay to a retirement program. Each employee also accrues 4 percent vacation pay based on the gross pay. Show computations.

Required

1. Enter the appropriate information in a payroll register.
2. Record the payroll information in the general journal, crediting net pay to Cash.
3. The employer's payroll costs include matching each employee's CPP contribution and paying 1.4 times the employees' EI premium. Record the employer's payroll costs in the general journal.
4. Why was there no deduction of CPP or EI for Dodge and no deduction of EI for Valenti?
5. What would be the vacation pay liability for Radii Video Productions Inc.?

Requirement 1

		PAYROLL REGISTER				
			GROSS PAY			
EMPLOYEE NAME	HRS.	STRAIGHT TIME	OVERTIME	TOTAL	INCOME TAX	CANADA PENSION PLAN

Calculations:

Calculations:

Requirement 1

PAYROLL REGISTER							
DEDUCTIONS			NET PAY		ACCOUNT DEBITED		
EMPLOYMENT INSURANCE	UNITED WAY	TOTAL	AMOUNT	CHQ. NO.	RETIREMENT PROGRAM	OFFICE SALARIES EXPENSE	SALES SALARIES EXPENSE

Requirements 2 & 3

General Journal

DATE		ACCOUNT TITLES AND EXPLANATIONS	POST REF.	DEBIT	CREDIT

Requirements 4 & 5

Problem 11-9A ① ② ⑤

Beaufort Explorations produces and sells customized mining equipment in New Brunswick. The company offers a 60-day, all parts and labour—and an extra 90-day, parts-only—warranty on all of its products. The company had the following transactions in 2017:

Jan.	31	Sales for the month totalled $80,000 (not including HST), of which 90 percent were on credit. The company collects 13 percent HST on all sales and estimates its warranty costs at 4 percent of sales.
	31	Based on last year's property tax assessment, the company estimated that the property taxes for the year would be $60,000 (3 percent of last year's $2,000,000 assessed value). Recorded the estimated property taxes for the month; credited Property Taxes Payable.
Feb.	4	Completed repair work for a customer. The parts ($500) and labour ($850) were all covered under the warranty. Record the labour as Wages Expense.
	7	Sent a cheque for the appropriate HST for the month of January (the company had paid $3,700 of HST on purchases in January).
	28	Recorded the estimated property taxes for the month of February.
	28	Sales for the month totalled $92,000 (not including HST), of which 85 percent were on credit. The company estimates its warranty costs at 4 percent of sales.
Mar.	7	Sent a cheque for the appropriate HST amount for the month of February (the company had paid $4,750 of HST on purchases in February).
	8	Beaufort Explorations received notice that it was being sued by a customer for an accident resulting from the failure of its product. The company's lawyer was reluctant to estimate the likely outcome of the lawsuit, but another customer indicated that a similar case had resulted in a $500,000 settlement.
	15	Completed repair work for a customer. The parts ($2,500) and labour ($1,200) were all covered under the warranty.
	21	Completed repair work for a customer. The parts ($750) were covered by the warranty, but the labour ($500) was not. Payment from the customer is due for the labour in 30 days.
	31	Sales for the month totalled $88,000 (not including HST), of which 90 percent were on credit. The company estimates its warranty costs at 4 percent of sales.
	31	Received the property tax assessment for 2017. It showed the assessed value of the property to be $2,200,000 and a tax rate of 3 percent of the assessed value. The company made the appropriate adjustment and used the Property Taxes Payable account. Property tax will be paid on December 31, 2017.

Required

1. Journalize the above transactions.
2. Show the appropriate financial statement presentation for all liabilities at March 31, 2017.

Requirement 1

		General Journal			
DATE		ACCOUNT TITLES AND EXPLANATIONS	POST REF.	DEBIT	CREDIT

Requirement 1 (Continued)

General Journal

DATE	ACCOUNT TITLES AND EXPLANATIONS	POST REF.	DEBIT	CREDIT

Requirement 2